BECOMING
An American Odyssey

BECOMING

An American Odyssey

A N D R E W   G O L D S T E I N

Saturday Review Press
New York

Published simultaneously in Canada by
Doubleday Canada, Ltd., Toronto.

Library of Congress Catalog Card Number: 72-88650
ISBN: 0-8415-0219-6 7 -12- 73

Saturday Review Press
380 Madison Avenue
New York, New York 10017

Printed in the United States of America

Design by Tere LoPrete

CONTENTS

Becoming: An American Odyssey Is an Impressionistic History of a Time of Change. The Dates, Names, and Facts Are True Within the Impression but the Impression Is Subject to Memory and Bias.

Meeting

I

Fat Bertha is watching. Watching me. Watching you. A deaf child named Amy is winking on a beach in Oregon and five years of change, five years of becoming. I am Goldstein boy becoming and Fat Bertha is watching.

I am a perimeter walking a beach in Oregon at the edge of America; but even in the thick curdling cheese of Wisconsin I was here along the edge. Five years of change and I have changed, but I am not one who plunges. I am bonded by love and nostalgia. Bonded by family, which flows through my blood.

You see, I grew up in Al's, a candy store in the Bronx, and a candy store in the Bronx is not a luncheonette in New Rochelle. A candy store is the beat of a neighborhood, the flux, the flow; a candy store is the bond where IF men come to IF, and fat ladies to drink thick chocolate malts and eat Drake's Pound Cake. Boys after playing punchball would come and pull out of ice-cold water Mission orange or black cherry, and munch a tall pretzel or a curled pretzel.

You climbed down four steps to enter Al's, a secret world beneath the sidewalk. In the summer evenings the bugs swarmed the entrance lights and in the hot humid sweat of July there were men who smoked cigars. IF men who huddled in green booths watching Yonkers Raceway on Al's TV. IF men, men of IF, and could have and would have, but never should have. Men of If Only and Daily Double and four-horse parley. These men screamed and cursed the horses, these men cursed their wives and called their bosses shmucks—these men knew everything from horses to football to stocks to politics, men who ate at Nedick stands and bet on tips from hot dog vendors. These were shoe salesmen and cutters and haberdashers, men of the Bronx who screamed in their three-room apartments for they were once boys of the Bronx with dreams and schemes, and in thirty years they had only progressed from the East Bronx to the West. There were some, Sol, Frank, Dave, who made it, moved to Westchester, Bayside, but the others were losers, men who never could. Once in a while a horse came in and there were egg creams on the house. Cigar smoke puffed happy smiles and the big winner bet it all on Silver Bullet in the third. "Oh" they screamed and banged the table and even Al bit through his cigar; but the smoke faded as Silver Bullet finished fourth. These were IF men, men of IF, men so close, almost, but in the end men not quite there. Men who never found the handle.

Outside Al's old ladies sat on Miami Beach aluminum chairs, flesh meshing in the plastic grid as trains above chunnnnnnnged and clunnnnnnnnnnnged men and women of the Bronx to Mosholu. Fat Bertha watched as little boys threw apple cores into the passing windows, little boys who rode with Mom and Dad to Yankee stadium where Mickey Mantle ran the bases as Willie Mays crashed into the Polo Grounds' wall six blocks away. The Jerome Avenue El, rusting brown, weaving the Bronx, and every day thousands passed my wall. The wall embracing Morris' tailor shop, Lou's barbershop, and Loy Ching's Chinese laundry. This same wall rebounded Spalding rubber balls as little boys played spud and handball. This wall anchored johnny-on-the-pony, and boxes were drawn for stickball, pitching pennies, flipping baseball cards.

Once playing King, Queen, Jack, Larry (who is king) slams the ball in my box shouting, without turning his head "I think your cousin Gary just got hit by a car." "Shut up fatso" I say, slicing the ball into his box. "I mean it" he says, sliding the ball high, skimming the wall. "On the corner." I turn to see a crowd huddling, Gary lying in the street beneath a fender. My eyes shoot up and there is Fat Bertha leaning shouting from her window "Who is it, who is it." I cannot see around the corner, but I know my mother is hanging out a fourth-story window across from Bertha, and I know she is going to kill me.

Beside the wall's pillaring, wide sidewalks distended

and old ladies sat and fat ladies gossiped wheeling shopping carts. Children played punchball, ringtoss, triangle, and the sidewalk embodied boxes and each box was a world to explore. The sidewalk was the flow of life, the IF men, the bookies, the canasta and gin players, the sidewalk was the mingle of the melt and no matter who you were young or old there was a stoop to sit on or play stoopball, a box to rest in or play boxball and a stair leading to Al's, a candy store to talk and drink egg creams, a rookery focusing the neighborhood.

Your father would walk, bakery box in hand, *Daily News* in arm and the cake was probably seven layer your favorite. You'd be playing off-the-stoop or touch football, Chevrolet to DeSoto, and you would see him walk slow after standing ten hours cutting ladies' dresses on 37th Street. He would ride the subway, sitting in the ethnic sweat and the sweat of rotting trains. He would walk the Grand Concourse where old men and old women sat on wooden benches circling Poe Park talking to themselves and others of seven-dollar sales at Alexander's. Down past Larry's Hardware he would shuffle and you would see him two blocks away and run toward and he would smile and you would straddle his waist and kiss his rough stubby face and his strength would feel good and his neck would smell good.

Later in the evening he would go to Al's, smoke a cigar, skim the racing sheet, and maybe place a bet. "Be up at eight" he says. "But Mom said eight-thirty" you say. "Eight" he says and you know and he knows and you know he is your father and you have to obey.

Barry Kahn was a boy many years older who lived at 18 East and once he walked over to our punchball game and asked if he could play. We said yes, excited to be playing with an older boy. When he was up I ran back, way back, back past the sewer, back past the safety zone, back to the curb, as far back as I had ever gone. Barry Kahn swung, and the ball rose faster and higher and higher over my head, bouncing in a Daitch-Shopwell shopping cart. And I do not know who or where Barry Kahn is today. I do not know if he is radical or conservative, hippie or straight. I only know Barry Kahn could punch a ball. And at a movie in Manhattan I met Peter the boy who had played trumpet to help his stuttering and he no longer stuttered or played trumpet, his hair was long and he studied at Ohio State. He said Lenny whose tremendous headlock ordained him ruler of the block was playing clarinet in a symphony orchestra and Kockerooni Kornfeld whose tooth I knocked out was still writing songs on his piano, and Lawrence the brilliant English boy who knew all the scientific terms for dirty words was a hippie in New York.

These boys were my life and we would play punchball, sewer to sewer, until my grandmother would call "Anddeeee eee Anddeee eeeee" and I would know dinner was ready.

My grandmother is old, only one eye still sees. My grandmother is old, only one ear still hears and her bones ache when it rains. She cries "Anddee, get me a hot water bag, hot towel, two aspirin." She is old and she slips on Good Humor sticks.

She rode the Grand Concourse bus to our house every day to clean and cook, and every meal she cooked she burned and every meal she cooked was the best she ever made. My sister, Barrie, and I would fight for the garbage bag, hiding burnt pot roast in napkins on our laps. Barrie would always sneak her burnt lamb chops onto my plate and when Grandma patrolled by, Barrie would say "Grandma, the meat is delicious, Mm good" and Grandma would poke her cataract eye so big in the glass, at my plate and say "How come you're not eating" and I would say "I am, Grandma, Mm delicious." Later in the evening, when my parents returned home after work, Grandma would run to the door and before my mother or father could slip off their coats she would halt them, grasp their arms and say "Guess what Andy and Barrie said tonight" and my mother exhausted from work would say "Mom, later, let me sit down first" and my father would poke my mother in the back and say "Get her out of here." Grandma, undaunted, blocked their passage and said "Guess what they said about my meal." My parents, cornered, succumbed, listening to Grandma swear on her life that we shouted "Grandma, this is the best meal I ever ate." Grandma would laugh and my father's ulcered stomach would gas as he anticipated the cold burnt lamb chops.

The burnt meat would sit on the unsavory plate flanked by cold potatoes which Grandma had fried with the lamb chops in Wesson oil. Grandma would parade the kitchen and repeatedly nudge my father with her elbow or palm and say "Some delicious meal, huh" and the tough meat would sink to my father's ulcered stomach as he nodded nauseously.

And everything she touched was the best, most of all her children. She would often accost strange people in the elevator and say "You know my daughter Lee" and the surprised person would say "I'm sorry, I don't" and Grandma would insist "Sure you do, the beautiful dark-haired girl, she has the handsome son Andy, my grandchild." The wary person, apprehensive, would say "Oh yes, I know her" and Grandma would say "Some beauty, huh." The stranger would cautiously say "Yes, a real beauty." In the evening after Grandma told my mother how delicious we thought her chicken was she would say "A very distinguished lady in the elevator spoke to me today. She said 'You're Rose Leight, aren't you?' and I didn't know who this lady was but I'm always friendly and I said 'Yes, I'm Rose Leight' and this lady, ooh, was she a fine lady, she said to me 'Rose Leight, your daughter Lee is the most beautiful girl I ever saw.' "

II

The children of the immigrants lived for the getting. Once gotten they colonized the suburbs. There were no walls or sidewalks in New Rochelle except for expedient pathways to stores, and no longer was there the flow of the Bronx block. Everyone lived in private homes with sectioned-off backyards. There were ball fields for the kids. Shopping centers for the shoppers. Every sphere was defined.

My parents joined the Tornado Beach Club and I worked at the Silver Springs, where ostentatious members in big Cadillacs and big cigars played cards all afternoon. I served hamburgers and saw the push of people afraid someone else was getting more pickles. I saw fat ugly ladies in silver swimsuits and rhinestone high heel sandals complain the rare hamburger was too rare, too well done, too, and the men fidgeted standing in the snack bar line in a constant vigilance searching for infringements of their money.

New Rochelle, populated by people moving at the speed of money, people whose lives were invested in a cabana and a cabana boy to set up the card table and serve ice water. New Rochelle, where my parents immigrated to give my sister and me good schools and ball fields. Grandma moved with us but traveled the Fordham bus back to her Bronx apartment on the weekends to be with her ninety-year-old boy friend, Mr. Korman. Though they had been dating for more than twenty-five years she still addressed him by his surname.

My school life was defined by the track team and daydreams. Lap after lap, I ran around the cinder track dreaming of Monica and Lauri, their naked bodies lying with me in the grass. Lap after lap, stomach tightening, legs cramping, a million excuses for quitting, but you go on lap after lap, a boy in defined awareness, lap after lap, you against you. In the winter, outside on banked boards ten above zero, you run in white shorts aware that your fingers are numb but the blood is circulating and you feel good and you experiment with slow strides, graceful stretches and you observe the klutzy guys running beside you and you know they are aware of your grace, you know they sneak envious glances and speak of you as THE DEER. Lap after lap, and Monica is sitting in your lap unbuttoning her blouse and Lauri is unzipping your pants and coach Pina is shouting, "Goldstein, what the hell are you doing out there" and you know that he is jealous of THE DEER.

You strut the halls aware of your presence and aware of others' aware and you hear them whispering, "That's Andy Goldstein THE DEER." Girls smile, say hello, and you smile or wave and you are aware of your body flowing. You are popular and funny and you love being loved. You love every hello and every laugh. Lap after lap, and you run until you vomit and then you run again.

In the spring you practiced every afternoon, best broad jumper and fastest white boy in New Rochelle High, and in the evenings you wrote sketches, auditioned talent, paced before the mirror acting sketches for the SENIOR VARIETY SHOW. Often intoxicated by the brilliance of your sketch, you would stand applauding or bowing as the applause deafened the bedroom. The show was a tremendous success and as you stood in the aisles being kissed, Lauri Adams embraced you and you desired to exclaim your love but others embraced, accolading, and she passed into the evening. For days afterward you could not work or sleep, reliving the show and you felt like Johnny Walsh felt throwing touchdowns, and the feeling was good. The feeling of walking through the halls with a girl you recently met and every pretty girl, every handsome boy says "Hello Andy" and you smile and say "Hi." The feeling of being Andy Goldstein, funny boy, track star, columnist, homeroom representative, Variety show star, the feeling of being THE DEER.

Lunchtime you would sit with the boys and

Richard, chewing a bologna sandwich, would whisper to Steve "Heard you screwed Judy over the weekend." Steve would blush his cheeks inundated with Bumble Bee Tuna Fish and say "Sh," but his blush would focus on each of us and in the lower smile of the blush there was pride; the table knew. And Douglas, chopped egg on Arnold's Brick Oven White, explained how he finger-fucked Sandy in a phone booth. You never liked this talk and after finishing your salami on rye you would go flirt with the girls, especially Monica. Monica, who migrated from Europe, was a cousin of Jeremy Wagner, president of the school, and she was different from the American girls, looser, freer, unrestrained. I was an American puritan defined by precepts and she was a free spirit. We argued every afternoon. I had always been this conservative moralist, even in junior high school I had developed a simplistic rigid epistemology with a guideline of rules for moral conduct; and a new religion was ignited, GOLDSTEINISM.

There were many followers but few devotees. Impious hypocrites, they still kissed in public, smoked cigarettes, and at a party Diane ran over to me saying "Andy, I'm so glad you're here, you're the only one who can liven up this party," and I smiled, mingled, told a few jokes and soon everyone was laughing, dancing. I danced with Diane, and Johnny Mathis sang "Chances Are," and while other couples kissed ears and lips, I did my Johnny Mathis imitation and Diane laughed, but later in the evening I sat alone in the dark corner chewing popcorn and testing the meltability of M&Ms as Stuey, the Judas of GOLDSTEINISM, humped Diane on the blue divan.

There is Diane, Monica and a myriad of crushes and infatuations melting in memory but incessantly vivid is Lauri. We met in typing class. I would glance toward her desk and pretend she was typing naked. Typing beside me she would lean brushing and sometimes in whisper wet my ear. Often she would slip her arm through mine as we promenaded the halls after typing class. My elbow would lean against her breast and I wondered if she were aware of the touch.

We launched a dingy sailboat on a windless day and paddled with our hands to a small island. We were alone and she wore blue short shorts and I still regret not kissing. She slipped her thumb between the elastic of her yellow panties and her tanned belly and with her other hand unzipped her fly and she pulled down her shorts and panties, down to her lower abdomen where the flesh lured white, and said "Look at that tan" and I said "Very nice."

Lauri's long-legged body lay laughing as the sun shadowed her bony face and we spoke of the Variety Show, donkey basketball, the Four Seasons' concert. We spoke of college and guessed who would flunk out and who would become famous. I said I wanted to be a writer or a stockbroker and she said she fancied being a psychologist like her father and I said "Me too." She said she would join a sorority at college and I said I would join a fraternity. We strolled, reminisced, and there were pauses where we almost touched, but we did not, and in the summer we said goodbye, goodbye to high school.

III

You buttonhook left on the dorm team and you march in groups of eight, ten, fourteen to the big game, Wisconsin against Michigan. Guys from Green Bay, Fond du Lac, Wausau, Twin Falls, Ashland, Indiana, Illinois, horsing around sneaking into dorm bathrooms to steal toilet paper to throw when the Buckeye Badgers score the big touchdown. And Richie Bogdanich jumps excitedly shouting "This town is going to burn tonight, they say it goes crazy when we win." You stand in section O with other freshmen singing "If you want to be a Badger just come along with me, by the bright shining light, by the light of the moon" and as Wisconsin advances into Michigan territory the cheerleaders tumble and flip and shout through megaphones as forty, fifty thousand spectators rise singing "On Wisconsin   On

Wisconsin fight on for her fame, throw the ball clear round Chicago, touch down, win this game, U Rah Rah" and before the game, before the screaming and throwing of toilet paper, before the emotions raging, there was hush and somber as the stadium rose to sing VARSITY. Fifty thousand arms pendulated back and forth in unison and the slow deep wail of VARSITY resounded the stadium, "Var si tee Var sit ee you rah rah Wiss conn sin, praise to thee we sing, praise to thee our al ma ma ta you rah ah rah Wi ih ssssss connnnn sinnnnnn."

We ate in the commons in groups of four, six, ten boys leering at girls on the food line. Jeff Bagley pointed to a beautiful blond girl and shouted "There she is, the one I told you about" and Paul Johnson, glancing says "Wow, she's gorgeous, look at those knobs" and Steve Lipman says "Hey Bagley is that the one you saw in bra and panties" and Bagley giggles saying "Heck no, I saw her in the raw." The table laughs. "I saw her slip that pretty blue towel off her head and sit combing her lovely blond hair" Bagley says and Richard Clarkston says loudly "Which hair" and the table roars.

Friday the boys from the dorm would cluster in groups of eight ten twenty and charge down State Street to the Badger Bar where they would challenge other tables to beer-drinking contests. Richard would leave our table smirking and we would cheer him standing by the bar ordering another pitcher. He would swivel winking at us and in the surreptitious stealth of dark crowded bar he would thrust his hand in passing crotch. The demure Wisconsin virgins from Neenah, Appleton, Baraboo, would blush and the table would pound with laughter. Later the boys would crowd into Bagley's room focusing the telescope on the girls' dorm and sit waiting, waiting for an open curtain, a shower, waiting.

At night I would study or relax in Bob's room as Mike bragged about laying this girl two minutes before curfew and Dennis told how this girl was in his pants before he even grabbed her tits. Sometimes we argued the Negroes and sometimes the Jews and sometimes my roommate Clarke and I would talk Vietnam but we both agreed America was right in intervening. Clarke was the son of the Daughter of the American Revolution and as moral as I was, he was more so. I often wished I had known him when GOLDSTEINISM was in its heyday. Neither of us smoked or drank and we usually laughed the evening away plotting ways to make our fortune. We planned to initiate a stock club and patent some toys we had invented.

During semester break we drove with our girl friends to Telemarck, Wisconsin, to go skiing. We found the most beautiful log cabins deep in the isolate woods where the temperature fell to forty below at night. We huddled close by the fire listening to the animals outside. There were no lights for miles and when we blew out the candles there was total darkness. My mind wandered to Monica and all the arguments over morality and sex. I thought of Suzie the beautiful Oriental girl I had dated till Christmas.

We would stand kissing along the wall of her dorm flanked by forty other couples kissing, sneaking hands up sweaters, humping against the wall as the clock raced toward midnight. The Telemarck woods echoed the darkness and our laughter split the night. We sat four in darkness head to belly listening to the vibrations and we laughed and laughed till the darkness closed our eyes and Clarke and I slept in one cabin, the girls in another.

Metamorphosis

I

You are there in the Mekong Delta. You are there with Alpha Company, a bunch of swell guys from all over the United States. Wyoming, Alaska, Nebraska, Rhode Island, Alabama, Idaho. There's some Viet Cong dead, three boys seventeen, sixteen, fif. And there's a Viet Cong stronghold, fire, fire, ceasefire. An old woman seventy-two dead. An old man sixty-six dead. An old. Texas, Montana, Kansas, Arkansas. And there is pain in you, hate for every Westmoreland, Johnson, Humphrey. Richmond, Montgomery, Boston, Boise. And look over there Corporal Philips, New Haven, Connecticut, is crawling attempting to save a Vietnamese girl. The Viet Cong are firing. But so are the American boys. Wisconsin, Pennsylvania, Oregon, Ohio. And terror in the scream of Vietnam girl as Philips' thigh gushes open. Davidson, New

York, McClosh, Iowa, grab his ankles dragging the dust flowing red, beading, and the wound twitching, fist beating, voice screaming, and you can see the muscle, the red pulp of a man.

The CBS cameraman unharmed focuses on the ligaments shattered, the veins pulsing and you are there inside Corporal Philips' right thigh. New ligaments tear and you are there below the muscle, beneath the pith, you are there watching the bone of a young soldier in the Mekong Delta.

You are there every night and there's WALTER and ERIC and Ike and George who died the other day and Harry when WALTER'S away and Dan and Roger and you are there in the Mekong Delta, there at Hamburger Hill, there at Tet, and there is ERIC telling the youth of today to be careful, a repression will come, the mindless sick radicals do not know, ERIC does, he is older, his teeth are rotting. You are there, only you are not, you are ten thousand miles away in the bourgeois womb of the Wisconsin Union surrounded by other bourgeois radicals laughing, mocking, aching.

You are me and you are watching WALTER. He is speaking of the dead. Eighty Americans. Nine hundred communists. The radical cynics are shouting "They're people, Walter, not communists." You are me and you are against the War In Vietnam, but have never acknowledged the depths of your rebellion. You are still the popular boy who all the neighbors love and you love going home to New Rochelle, visiting the Graybars, the Janowitzes; and the druggist calls you cow man, repeating the same joke every vacation and Frank the grocer shakes your hand and says "I hear you've been having some trouble out there, a few punks spoiling it for everybody" and Wendell the laundry man across the street is afraid for his kids.

You are me listening to David Keene, leader of the Wisconsin Young Americans for Freedom, you are me arguing with Bob Cohen, ranting against the war in the Union, you are me listening to Professor Mosse say he is against the war but America can't just pull out, big powers don't operate that way. You are me listening, reading, talking, screaming, you are me boy becoming.

You are watching an American helicopter being shot down by the North Vietnamese and the radicals sitting in the Union lounge are laughing, winking, applauding. Every night they sit in their Wisconsin Union cadre joking, mocking Johnson or the Lieutenant being interviewed and you sit hating them but the hate is a lie for you are they, quieter, less blatant, but you are they and they are you and you are all impotent middle-class clowns...............
Far From Vietnam.

You are they and you are watching Vietnam and every night you see the ten-inch TV images die and every night WALTER reads the score, and there are close-ups, interviews with the stars, highlights and instant replays, and on Sundays the lounge overflows with rooters for GREEN BAY against, they scream and cheer every time Bart Star throws the ball, and

Westmoreland says the gooks are on the run, defeated, Captain Williams, Arkansas, says the gooks are on the run, defeated, and you are watching an American helicopter being shot down and it is not easy for you to admit you are against GREEN BAY.

You were not raised on Tom Hayden, Bob Dylan, Black Panthers, SDS, LSD. When you were a child there was Al's where you would go after a Little League game dressed in your gray baseball uniform lettered "Tony's Pizza Parlor" and you'd order an egg cream as the clouds of smoke puffed and there was Willie Mays, Mickey Mantle, Y. A. Tittle, and college students were the Hunter girls you fell to the ground in fake hurt to see under their skirts and you hid on the roof dropping water balloons on them. And Grandma would sit in her blue chair singing Jewish folk songs or American love songs as you sat beside her stroking her baby-skin chin. She sang "All of meee why not take alll of meeeee, Can't you see I'm no goot without you, All of meeeee" and in the summer she would vacation in the Catskills with her ninety-year-old boy friend, Mr. Korman. She would always return complaining how old Mr. Korman was, bragging how popular she was at the hotel, "You should see when I walk in the dining room. Everybody stops eating. All the men leave their tables and come to see me and say 'Mrs. Leight you're so young. Mrs. Leight you're such a beautiful woman,

---

what are you doing with that old fogey, Come with me, I'll take you to Florida.' "

And when you were a child someone who got high was SUPERMAN. SUPERMAN who could bend steel with his bare hands, leap tall buildings at a single bound, fly faster than a speeding bullet. SUPERMAN disguised as Clark Kent, mild-mannered reporter, could be us, any young American boy with glasses and a phone booth. SUPERMAN fighting a never-ending battle for truth, justice, and the American Way.

You are the child of SUPERMAN and Howdy Doody and it was not easy for you to admit America was wrong, not easy to realize you felt pride when the North Vietnamese resisted GREEN BAY. You are a boy becoming a man and you are torn by ache. You are full of extreme emotions eating at you, and it is not easy after eighteen years of fervent belief in SUPERMAN to go out and search for kryptonite.

II

A student will sit one evening on the rocks of Lake Mendota. He will be lonely, hurt or sad. She will be becoming and the stillness of the waters and the patterns in the light will hold her in the evening, a cradle rocking softly. The blue water will call and the student will walk along the edge in isolate awareness. A laughing couple will saunter by shattering the perfect stillness; and again slowly the quiet will piece together. Time will fold down adding to the heavy and life will seem so strange. So much. Too much in one day. A thousand feelings, a million emotions. Alone in the become. Alone in the stillness the hand will grip a stone and the stone's texture will be soft and warm. In the stillness the student will smile knowing he is, she is, not alone. Once before, the stone was touched, touched by me.

I would sit on a red stool in the rathskeller watching the flow of the become. The rathskeller was a hub of MOVEMENT ideas, students would sit reading Marcuse or Malcolm X or Hermann Hesse or Frantz Fanon or Norman O. Brown or R. D. Laing and they would discuss Bob Dylan, the Beatles, socialism, Hegel, Nietzsche and they would describe their trips on marijuana, mescaline. No one really knows when the MOVEMENT began. Some say it was Rosa Parks and the bus boycott in Selma. Some say it was Mario Savio and the free speech movement in Berkeley. And some say it began with Jesus. The MOVEMENT is a conglomeration of misfits, neurotics, malcontents, romantics, visionaries, adventurers, and in the rathskeller the bodies flowed loose in freedom and tense in search. The rathskeller vibrated in the excitement of conceit. The rathskeller dark with brown arches leading to high-domed ceiling and in the corner by the cashier blacks sat conspiring to reestablish their culture and nearby Richie, The Penguin, as he was known because of his peculiar penguinese walk, sold nickel bags of marijuana and day and night the rathskeller crawled like a vast dark web of insects as the boys hopped from tables searching for lays, and fraternity boys grew mustaches and sat pretending to read *Being and Nothingness* sneaking peeks at the braless short-skirted girls.

The rathskeller searchers still possessed the infatuation with themselves. They still were trying to outcool each other. Their search was not the quiet journey but the intense search of search itself, the intense search of being consciously searching, looking for answers, and some found the cure-all with Marx, others with astrology, others with Yoga and some took the journey East with Hesse. Many discovered the god Mescalito and others found God in the land. You could see the nervous need to be part of, the desperation in the tense neurotic movements, but pervasive was the search, the transcending of the Jell-O.

Faces pass me in a day wondering which way and I am Goldstein boy becoming a man and I do not know. I have licked soft ice cream and witnessed fifty protesters multiply and swell into a movement of thousands. I have seen Bob Cohen stand alone in a one-man protest of the Peace Corps in 1966. I have seen Seymour booed and hooted sway an audience to cheers. And in the fall of '66 I saw fifteen boys sit in a circle outside the rathskeller on the terrace. The lake was choppy and only two sailboats dared the wind. The boys were discussing their lives and the draft and they were forming a WE WON'T GO committee and a list of names to be submitted to the newspaper. Fifteen young men in the fall of '66 and they gained strength from each other and others gained strength from them and soon there were more names and for every name there was there were a hundred others who did not sign but who would not go and it was nice to know you were not alone.

In the evening the rathskeller would overflow and the movement was freer than high school but there was a conscious awareness in every quote, in every nod of head to "Sergeant Pepper's" blasting and an obviousness in the parade. Each table competing to be the Messiah. Each table believing they were the Messiah, believing the millennium was verging and they were the chosen people come to resurrect the world of love and freedom. The searchers listened as the adventurers brought back treasures from their trips to Europe, India, drug land, the stars, the earth, and each trip brought back valuables to be assimilated in the new world. But sitting in the rathskeller was an old man wearing red sneakers and playing bridge. No one in the Movement ever asked "What's an old man wearing red sneakers and playing bridge doing in the rathskeller?" He was invisible to the Movement, for the Movement was happening now, and the old man who also wore a yellow vest was always there, even in the quiet fifties.

You would walk the lovely lake path surrounded by oak and lake and you would try to understand the rathskeller, the MOVEMENT, and there were no answers. You would think of high school so far away and try to focus on the day you changed, but the days melted into somewhere sometime and you were obsessed with the wonder of becoming, the wonder of growing up and becoming a person. Enmeshed in odyssey, in the conceit of youth, it was difficult to focus, to comprehend the stirring. The MOVEMENT pervasive shrouding engulfing and the rathskeller oozed in thick swabbing throbs of intensity. And sometimes the thick heavy suffocated and out to the lake the need, the need to focus, to stop time. The need to still the night and you would skip rocks and run the shore and sing "I am I Don Quixote the Lord of La Mancha my destiny calls and I go" and a girl would pass by laughing and sing "I am I Sancho Panza I follow my master" and laughing in the round you would sing "And the wild winds of fortune will carry me onwards" and she would laugh and say hello. She would be from Prairie Du Chien or Baraboo and she would live in Elizabeth Waters, the conservative women's dorm on the other side of campus where all the football players lived and the agricultural and business students who never deigned to nestle in the rathskeller. She would be a pretty Wisconsin virgin named Joannah and she would like to sail and ride her bike. She would know nothing of Vietnam or Bobby Seale or marijuana. She would say, "Gosh you're funny" and you would say "Joannah, I am Don Quixote de La Mancha and my quest is not that of humor, I have been dubbed the knight of night and my spells are cast in the dark somber seriousness of dangerous death." You would spin and jump a bench and lead Joannah to the water where you would sprinkle her in baptism and say the magic words, "Zeeno Zango, Wheeemi Lumbo and all the other Gods of the Congo make this lady my minion" and she would ask "What's a minion?" and you would answer "Cousin to an onion" and she would laugh and you would laugh and we would stroll talking of the woods of Baraboo.

III

It is the spring of 1966 and Madison is so beautiful in the spring after the long cold Wisconsin winter. The arboretum is budding and if you sit quietly behind a certain bush you may watch the mating of the woodcock. It is a splendid thing indeed. They sing and dance, twirl and spin for they are in love with life. Young lovers bicycle through shrubs and others more daring lie beneath a bush or in the shade of the pine forest and kiss and maybe even if it is a quiet day unbutton each other and make love.

You are against the war in Vietnam and play football on the mall with Bob Cohen, Billy Simons and other Big Radicals On Campus, but have never protested and have decided to devote the spring to getting your tennis serve back in form. You skip down State Street in your white tennis shorts, old

Happy Doodah himself. A pretty sorority girl from Freshman English class smiles Wisconsin cheese and says "Hi, how areya" and you smile your sunny face and say "Fine, how are you" and she smiles wider "I'm fine too" and you smile broader "That's fine too" and you skip down the street searching for other girls to scintillate.

You are Happy Doodah but there is a tension in the air, a feeling of being out of place in your tennis shorts. Protesters are leafleting about a draft protest at the administration building and clusters form outside the university book store, arguments, debates, and there is an excitement of being on the verge of, an excitement that would intensify that evening, an incipient excitement that would ebb and charge, increase and wane over the next five years, but would always be there, an apprehension, a volatile miasma, invisible but waiting.

The administration building overflowed with students, long hair, short hair, bearded, fraternity, sorority and only eight months before you played left end on the dorm team and good liberal Americans were raising families with Tom selling newspapers, and Debbie trick or treating for UNICEF. Fifty filthy protesters give 'em a cause, a sign, you'll find someone to complain. And soon there were sixty. A few leaflets, seventy. Debates in the Union, eighty. Liberal Americans thought the noise unnecessary. After all Johnson did a lot for civil rights and Humphrey was right there. Two hundred. If the war was wrong Johnson would know. Filthy sick communist dupes. Five hundred. Good clean American boys helping freedom and a thousand students jammed the administration building. The radical leaders after months of being spit upon, beat upon, were euphoric with power, with being part of a MOVEMENT.

For the first time the fraternity and sorority mingled with the bearded, the searchers, and at last a mass campus rally. And in the mingle and touch the stereotypes were discarded and sandwiches were shared and the excitement intensified as the speakers harangued. Smaller arguments broke out around the room and there was a need, a need to talk, to touch the person beside you and talk. Caucuses met outside and frenetic movement weaved in the febrile flow of vibrations. There was an abandon of conscious awareness, abandon of trying to impress, we were moving too fast to calculate or manipulate, we were moving at the speed of verge, and there was only feeling, emotion, need.

The leaders fought each other to the microphone, and parliamentary rules controlled the chaos as we debated whether to block the doors or just sit-in. You sat in nervous need sweating, standing, sitting, jumping, screaming and touching the boy you fought with, the girl you agreed with, and as each speaker argued you argued back and a thousand voices cursed and yelled and a thousand students vibrated the verge, the feeling of being part of, and the vote to sit in unobstructively won, and you cheered and kissed and hugged and your body flowed in euphoria, flowed in the feeling of being part of a MOVEMENT.

IV

My grandmother did not understand what was happening in one of her soap operas. I tried to explain that the girl decided not to marry because she was going blind. My grandmother began to cry, not for the girl, or because she too was almost blind, but because she did not understand. You see, she is old and her friends have died. She is old, she has seen the benches full.

She is old but she cooks and cleans and tells my mother to go to bed and stop staying out late every night. She is old and she falls on buses, on holes in the sidewalk, on A&P dollies. She falls, complains, and dreams of suing and becoming rich.

When you were sick she would sit beside you rubbing her palm along your forehead and she would wind string mysteriously into a cat's cradle game. She would tell stories of your mother as a child and Grandma would laugh recalling her beautiful brilliant little girl. But her voice would harden and she would spit and say "Phew, look what she married" and her head would shake loathing "So many wonderful boys wanted to marry her, Freddie Sachs such a good boy, phew this moron, this pig she married" and Grandma could be the most wonderful warm considerate lady and she could joke and laugh but always even in the broadest smile a thin line of her lower lip echoed bitterly.

She is old and she watches Judge Forbes blackmail Mike Carr. She knows who is pregnant, who is divorced. She weeps and laughs living in the afternoon from two to four. But now she does not understand and she sits shaking. She raises the volume of her hearing aid, holds my hand as I slowly repeat the events, the plot, and she slowly fills in details. And soon she is there, she understands, and she laughs and wipes her face with a dishrag.

She is happy to have her little Andala home again and her little Andala is glad to be back home. Her little Andala will work at the Silver Springs Club again and practice his death weapon serve again, but it will not be the same. Her little Andala has sat in the administration building as the administrators walked by laughing at the dummies sitting on the floor. Her little Andala has lost the desire to serve the rich, her little Andala has lost the desire to sit with his parents and their friends every Sunday evening dining at the club talking of Thelma Ludlow and Betty Weinberg making fools of themselves at the bar chasing Seymour Lipsky.

As the late sun dialed eight little Andala would say "I'm going home" and Mother would say "Aren't you eating with us" and little Andala would say "No, I'll eat at home" and Mother would say "There's nothing to eat at home" and little Andala would say "There's some salami, I'll make sandwiches" and Mother would say "Isn't that crazy, you could have steak here, delicious parfait you love" and Father would say "He's a nut, you know he's a nut, let him go."

The nut would walk the road as the Cadillacs, Lincolns, Oldsmobiles passed him full of gin players and canasta players exhausted from a hard day at the card table. The nut would eat kosher salami watching "Bonanza" and try to discern what was happening. Kenny told you about his LSD trip where he talked with little mauve men sitting on the bark of a maple tree, and Steve's parents found out he was smoking marijuana, and you were still Andy Goldstein, oh sure you called yourself Andrew now and you protested the war but you were still a good boy, and your father called you nut, but that he always did. You were still Andy Goldstein the happy nut and there was this feeling that even if you were to totally change, grow a beard, long hair, turn on every day, you would still be Andy Goldstein. You had changed tremendously from the GOLDSTEINISM days, but there were moments of immutability, a constant essence echoing in every radical action.

You walked the streets of New Rochelle and you were still the high school kid. You met Doug Peters at

Macy's and he told you he belonged to Alpha Theta
Tau and Larry Greenberg married Marsha Stone and
.... and it was good to hear, nice to
touch the memory. Wet tongues on a Friday afternoon locked in a 1956 DeSoto in Cross County
Shopping Center as you and Marsha Stone kissed and
petted and wet tongues on a Friday afternoon as only
the year before you and Lauri Adams cut class and
• ate hamburgers in the doughnut shop and imagined
college life and wet tongues on a Friday afternoon.
You rendezvoused with Monica and kissed and
hugged and she told you her entire floor at Barnard
had been virgins in the fall but after months of
Monicanese only two of twelve girls remained to be
deflowered and you spoke of Vietnam, the rathskeller, the change, but even she was not prepared.
Ideas were fermenting in the rathskeller that would
polarize a nation. Ideas insidiously capturing a generation and isolating them from the society, isolating
them in a hunger for the materialization of their
dreams and these dreams were unfulfillable in the
existing space, dreams transcending the definitions of
the existing milieu. Atavistic dreams bonded to a
primitive vision, streaking beyond, beyond our grasp.
These were dreams intrinsic to the ideas and Monica
and I could reminisce, we could attempt compre-
hension and speak of the future, but our words were
finite, limited to the concepts of our society, and in
the rathskeller were ideas infinite, for madmen only.
Ideas transcending the liberal rational mind of ERIC
SEVAREID. In the rathskeller was the beyond, ovulating, waiting, waiting.

V

Dow was the turning point of radical life at the University of Wisconsin. Dow happened in October of '67. Before Columbia. Before Chicago. The Vietnam war protest had grown tremendously from a few radicals to a campus movement. The majority of the students, as WALTER loved to say, still studied in the library instead of being loud exhibitionists, but a peace march would attract several thousand instead of only fifty.

And it is strange the way things are, I mean like the first war protesters who stood alone in '64 and '65 when we laughed and spit and called them communists. Many were sick, neurotic, lost, alienated. Many were haters, mean, sadistic. But it was they who were the moral voice. The good healthy students drank beer and goosed Job's Daughters. The healthy

Americans walked in silver hair and tennis shoes eating lobsters along Martha's Vineyard. Healthy people camped in Estes Park and packed their kids in Ford Falcon wagons traveling the Rockies and the Smokies. Healthy families vacationed at Atlantic City where the two out of three bust-the-balloon dart players flung their dimes at crippled men who shouted in froggy voices "Win a doll, here's a baton little girl" and Mom and Dad chewed salt-water taffy and tried their luck placing quarters on number nine which never came as the wheel clicked only one away, and "Oh" they screamed "How close" and another Mom and Dad strolled the boardwalk splintering above the ocean and the Dad said "Smell that air" and the Mom said "Mm good" and the Dad said "It's a good life" and the Mom said "I know" and the healthy psychiatrists so ready to diagnose the young skied Aspen and Jackson Hole and drank Khahlúa in silent passivity.

We saw the Robert Cohens, Billys, Karens, we saw people we did not like, egotistic, condescending people who talked loud and snuck in movie lines, people who shouted and cursed for it was the only way to be heard above the ominous silence.

In October of '67 Commerce Hall overflowed sardined with students protesting the war, protesting Dow Chemical interviews on campus. Outside the building a crowd was growing, a crowd of sympathizers and taunters. Small arguments broke out and the students who had gathered to spit and call the protesters communists and hippies as they were dragged out of the building smiled at the police who stood immobile across the street dressed in white hooded helmet and beige club.

The university police chief shouted through a bull-horn "You have five minutes to vacate the building. You are obstructing the freedom of other students and are on private property. You must leave the building in five minutes or be arrested." Inside was introspective tremor, apprehension, it was the first time city police were participating in a campus disturbance. From the building a muffled voice shouted "We are not leaving this building till we have a signed statement from Chancellor Sewel that the Dow interviews will cease on property belonging to the University of Wisconsin."

Outside half the crowd booed while the other half applauded wildly. Across the street underneath the Carillon tower the police fidgeted preparing for the confrontation. My class on Shakespeare was starting in five minutes but I decided to skip it. I stood near the glass doors and could see students preparing to barricade. The bullhorn clicked and the chief said "This is our last warning, you have two minutes." The tension thickened and the crowd distended to over a thousand and across the street the immutable frozen Blue statue broke and began to move. Hundreds applauded as the Blue marched in rows of eight and clubs raised as the Blue stepped over the curb and the crowd flanked the pathway and the Blue began to shove and push the crowd back and the pathway widened as the rows of eight trotted and a bearded boy shouted "Hey look they're taking off their badges" and club whacked bearded boy, whacked head, downing him and others shouted and other clubs split the air, and the police continued to march.

Hysteria swept the crowd and now there was terror and hush as the glass smashed and the swish of club pendulated up and down, up and down, into head, shoulder, breast, thigh, and inside locked tight in the crush were screams and outside you saw wood splinter and you stood crying paralyzed with hate and disbelief as the crowd began to boo. The police swung, stampeding the crowd backward and the Boo horrified, the Boo confused pitched higher and higher and the fraternity boys who had come to taunt and spit stood in silent horror until instinctively the Boo crept through their throats, the Boo sweeping spreading and the hate intensifying and the Boo embodying our hate and the Boo engulfing and the dissonance intensely melted into consonance, into one harmonious BOO.

We were not prepared. There had been no Columbia or Chicago. The protesters did not bring rocks or knives, they had come to be arrested. And you came to watch, a voyeur radical protesting vicariously. You came to watch, for you could not justify the blocking of doors, the infringement of freedom. You had seen the napalmed babies, chins melted into chests but you came to watch and horror gripped you, horror and hate.

It was the end of belief and it murmured. Gripped in hate the murmur of change of radical epiphany.

You came to watch and the hate watched you and tossed you and hate etched in every face, hate in the savage swing of the club, hate in the chant "Fascist Pigs, Fascist Pigs, Pigs, Pigs, Fascist Pigs" and the chant intensified into a loathing wailing metronome and six students surrounded the university police chief who had desired to be the students' friend and they shouted "You pig, Hanson, you filthy fucking pig, you fucking filthy fascist pig" and he stared at the cracks in the sidewalk, it was no longer in his control.

Tear gas shot for the first time on campus, tear gas dispersing the crowd, tear gas permeating classrooms, evacuating lectures, and down the hill thousands crying, tearing, mingled with the fleeing and people shouted "What's happening, What's happening" and panic bumped and moaned and students fell to the grass to rub their eyes and vomit. And other students cried "Don't rub your eyes, Don't rub your eyes" and Sharon and Steve bent over to ask if I was all right and I said yes just overwhelmed and they shook their heads and we walked together as thousands ran down the hill like the peasants in *Potemkin* and Steve and Sharon said they had learned a lesson, next time they would be prepared, rocks, clubs and knives.

Down the hill too much in one day and the hate flowed deep, as deep as I would ever know, a hate indelible eating away the bonds, eating away the love. A hate called from the depths of my person freeing me from the past, and the hate would recede in time, the hate would mellow, the images would be forgotten, but the hate was indelible, and in the tear gas vapor, in the miasma the hate hung staining Bascom Hall and the miasma's pungency would disappear in a few hours, a few days, but the stains would scar, holding the hate in dormancy, hate that would not leave Wisconsin for years. There would be moments of conciliation but the hate was there waiting to be triggered, hate indelible dormant waiting.

VI

There is always love, for I am bonded. Bonded by memory and touch. Bonded by my mother father sister grandmother. Even after Dow you would return at Christmas to lie in your parents' bed between your mother and father and your mother would be knitting a sweater for her expectant first grandchild and your father watching television and you would talk of school, friends, and the conversation would be warm unless the topic turned to drugs or Vietnam. Your mother liked to think of herself as a liberal because she gave the colored cleaning girl her old clothes and she argued against the war at the canasta game. But she did not want to hear of your demonstrating. Your father loved to shout "Communist" to rile you, but though he hadn't read a book in twenty years he bought *Vietnam: The Logic of Withdrawal* because he wanted to understand and be able to talk to his son and there is family flowing in his touch. Every hit, every punch, every derisive insult, moron, idiot, is how a nonverbal IF man says I Love. And you lie in bed telling him that your girl friend is Catholic, you will not serve in the army, will continue to protest the war and will never be the stockbroker he wants you to be and you can hear his ulcer churning for he is Irv Goldstein, who has stood on his feet ten hours a day, six days a week, for this, this moron, this idiot, and he looks at his wife who has worked all her married days to help pay the bills and send the kids to college and he smiles and she laughs and you touch his hairy chest and he grimaces in revulsion "Get away from me, you moron, go to your mother, you're her son" and your mother puts down her knitting and says "Now he's my son, you can have him" and he says "I don't want him, he's all yours, send a kid to college three years and he's dumber than when he started" and Grandma watching Red Skelton in the living room comes in to make sure we're not conspiring against her and your father says "Oh, here she is, another genius, Hey, Rosie, here's your grandson, take him away" and Grandma laughs saying "You can have him with that long hair, feh look at him, it's that lousy Wisconsin" and your father squeezes your thigh as Grandma harangues and this is family and it flows through your blood, flows bonding you to the bourgeois order.

Love flowing as Grandma lights the Friday night sabbath candles with the dishrag on her head, love flowing as she asks you to call her as she bathes and you call "Grandma, are you all right" and she laughs in the tub and says "Yes Andala, thank you." Love flowing as your father smokes his big cigar on the tennis court and you serve the ball six inches in his box and he yells "Double fault, my game" and love talking with your mother at the breakfast table as she discusses the two thousand dollars she owes the bank and even as a child she confided in you and fought with your father out front, for we were more than parents and children, we were family sharing the saga and you knew no matter what you did you could go to her and she might be angry or hurt but if you came and spoke honestly she would understand and now you would talk about sex and drugs and Vietnam and you would argue and anger but you would always forgive, for this is the way it is in family. Family, a current binding you to a nation, a flow intrinsic to your every gesture, an essence—family—and you cannot escape, you cannot break the bonds, you are Goldstein bonded to family and you cannot plunge.

Your sister and you challenge Mom and Dad to a Scrabble game and your father screams at everyone who spends more than a minute thinking of a word, except he ponders five minutes sneaking glances at the dictionary and finally he smiles and places on the triple score the word "krezle" and you laugh and Barrie laughs and your mother laughs and he screams "You idiots, krezle is a spool of yarn, we use it in the cutting room" and your hand reaches for the dictionary and his hand slaps yours and he says "Don't you trust your father"... family and it flows in every motion of my grandmother, every call of Andala, every bitter diatribe, every weep, flows as she struts down the aisle of my sister's wedding, an eighty-something-year-old woman too vain to tell her age, lips pursed, smiling down the aisle bosom thrusted believing that everyone is whispering "Look at Mrs. Leight, isn't she amazing, isn't she beautiful, look how young she is" and she gestures dramatically placing her palm on hip for the picture believing that four hundred eyes are focusing on her and her beautiful daughter and her beautiful granddaughter and her handsome grandson and they are all admiring what an extraordinary woman she is and she is THE DEER.

VII

Sharon would slip into my room at night as I lay in bed reading *Beyond Good and Evil,* or sleeping. Her hands would press against my naked chest or back or thighs and she would massage. We would talk of art or sex or drugs or relationships or Vietnam. Everyone in the house, except for her and me, was smoking marijuana and dropping mescaline, and she would tell me of her virgin years and I would tell of mine. I would tell of the year before, living with Tom, Carl, and Roger, three virgin boys from Neenah, Wisconsin. We lived on Mifflin Strect in the fall of '66 when the anti-war movement was still incipient and experiment with drugs and life-style was still confined to a cluster.

Joshing in the evening Tom would say "Hey Rog, saw you with that cute little waitress today" and Rog would giggle smiling, a little pixie puppet face saying "What waitress" and Tom would say "Look at Mr. Innocent here" and I would say "Was she the short sexy black-haired girl" and Tom would laugh his tight engineering chuckle yes and Roger would shout loudly "Come on you guys, I'm trying to study about cell differentiation and you know I wasn't with any waitress today" and Carl would say "That's not what I heard, Rog, I heard she's pretty nice and" and Roger would blush his puffy Neenah cheeks, slam his biology text closed and say "Gosh you guys, ooo you guys make me so mad, you know I wasn't with any waitress today" and Tom would say "Rog, if all three of us saw you, come on be honest" and Roger would giggle, his face red shouting "You guys oooo oooooo you guys, come on where does she work, come on you guys." . . . And Sharon would belly-laugh lying in bed beside me while the beautiful blond Rose Marie made love to the trumpet player in the room below. And when he was traveling with his rock band the beautiful blond Rose Marie filled her loneliness with Arlon Gorman who shared her bath. The beautiful blond Rose Marie liked to lie naked on the roof and often she and the trumpet player and Arlon Gorman and others needing night or high would climb the rotting ladder and turn on to the stars. I would lie in bed listening to the patter of their steps and they would tap my window smiling, laughing, stoned, and King Lear would sit before me rambling words that jingled incoherently as my mind tried to comprehend the change.

I was living in this beautiful hundred-and-seven-year-old house built before the Civil War and I shared my bath with Sharon and Ted and Mary and they brought Phil and Steve and Barbara. This house which once saw Abraham Lincoln and once housed the governor of Wisconsin still stood gray and haunting, hovering above the lake. Only now it housed the beautiful blond Rose Marie and the trumpet player and Arlon Gorman and Derik the homosexual artist and Martin another artist who supposedly was Derik's secret love but who was sleeping with a fourteen-year-old Madison Junior High School girl named Louise.

And in the fall of '67 it was all kind of exciting, kind of new, there was a thrill in living in the same house with girls and involved in a life-style that was once called Bohemian but would soon be middle class. Only the year before I had lived with three virgin boys who did not smoke marijuana, did not sleep with girls, did not experiment or dare. Three Wisconsin boys who believed the United States was right in Vietnam and we would argue and laugh and anger but we could still be friends. There was still space to josh in the evening and time to believe in America. In three years Mifflin Street would become MIFFLAND, a radical ghetto.

There had always been radicals living in the area but in the fall of '66 there was still space for others, still space to live a normal life. Tom, Carl, Roger could study chemistry, engineering, economics and plan on going to graduate school, earning a master's or doctorate, earning ten, fifteen, twenty thousand dollars a year and buy a home, raise a nice family. But somewhere sometime that space was eliminated and long hair and drugs and drugs and guns and bombs and paranoia and paranoia and hate and love and hate occupied the space. The colors, textures, language changed, eliminating the words and forms for dreams within the society. No longer was there space to talk innocently in the evening. There was only thick and intense and search and intense thick search. There was only MOVEMENT and the MOVEMENT engulfed Miffland negating joshing space.

You tried to articulate to Sharon your feeling of tremendous subtle change. Intangible change. It was more than not being a virgin anymore, more than living in a house with girls, more than the smell of marijuana and cat shit. A feeling that even if you were living the most middle class of lives, even in the future if you were to buy a house and raise a family, somewhere sometime there was a change indelible. You had entered an entirely new perspective.

You lay with Sharon and you had lain with Lauri Adams in high school on her couch, your toes leaning against her breasts, and your arms embracing her toes. You studied American history as she studied the history of the world and you spoke of the senior prom; but there was a feeling lying with Sharon that somewhere sometime in the space between the two images the space had changed. You and Lauri and Sharon filled the space with the sound of your laughter and desire and doubt and fear and dreams and the sound echoed loud and soft and lullabied and cried and howled, and the sound was similar, related, but the silence told another story, the silence told of change. In the space between the sound life had altered and would never be the same.

VIII

You are sitting in GREAT HALL listening to the pumped-in voices of the university faculty meeting. The voices are discussing the Dow demonstrations and one by one the distinguished brilliant scholars articulate eloquent explanations and rationalizations. Few of the speakers were at the demonstration but they are caught in the myths and lies. A society has defined them as an elite intellectual force, as savants, and they are caught in the definitions. On and on they maunder and the faculty applauds. They truly believe they are contributing intelligent dialogue and perhaps if I had not been at Dow, if I had gone to my Shakespeare lecture, I would listen to these articulate words, these pros and cons, and I would analyze the logic, decipher the arguments. . . . .
. . . . And it is the way of epiphany that you

break through a fog and see not something newly
arrived or just polished, but something dull, and there
all the time. Something just waiting for the right
mood, the right combustion. You see what you have
always known in the deep dark instincts hidden
beneath the lies. Perhaps you are talking with a
friend, talking at the speed of the lie and suddenly
you are moving at a different speed and you see the
words you have been uttering and they are the
broken pieces of a jigsaw puzzle. Perhaps you are
walking into a room full of people, walking at the
speed of the lie and suddenly an instinct in you slows
down or speeds up and you are a spectator of yourself. You see the conscious movements, the awkward
gestures. Or perhaps you are a young boy becoming a
man sitting in GREAT HALL surrounded by other
young people engaged in becoming, listening to words
pumped through speakers and suddenly you can see
the words falling out of the speakers, like the letters
of the alphabet falling, like the falling of
Cheerios............................. You
are sitting with Professor Stalworth as he defends the
university requirements and you tell him you are
wasting, suffocating in the boredom, and he tells you
a student needs a liberal education. He explains how
after the Russians landed Sputnik American uni-
versities stressed science and foreign language and he
smiles throughout his articulate discourse and you say
it is all very rational and maybe one day you will love
geology or German but now you are wasting, not
remembering one foreign word, one rock, and he

smiles and says "That's up to you, we offer education" and you know that is bullshit. You know the
university is a lie and the professors support that lie
and immersed in one lie they defend with another
and the lie grows engulfing, grows and grows and the
lie becomes the life, the accepted norm, and engulfed
in lie they see only within the lie and the lie grows
and grows.... And One Fine Morning... and one
fine morning you wake up sweating in contempt,
contempt for this impostor sitting before you smiling,
articulating rational answers as you guttulate the
feeling of waste and he is smiling talking about education and he is not hearing that you are wasting and
the waste eats at your psyche and you are not alone,
you are part of a feeling of despair and hate and
contempt and nausea, part of a witness to the lie and
a revulsion and the man is smiling for he really
believes he is your friend. You are wasting and he is
smiling, the smile of smiles, the smile of the dean, the
smile of the adviser, the smile of the liberal rational
mind remembering when he was young and was a
rabble-rouser and how a teacher once smiled at him
and said "You're young and a rabble-rouser but in
time you'll see" and he saw, and now he is smiling
this smile at me, and he says "Surely, Mr. Goldstein
we have rules here, you cannot expect us to break
them for you, this is a large university, everyone is
equal, and I can well understand, there were many
courses in college I did not like, but I got by, it's"
and the contempt is a wave triggered, an overwhelming
paralyzing contempt, and it is not merely the con-

tempt of the moment, but moments weaving the lie, moments face to face with the crack, and moments when you burst from the Jell-O and see the lie and the man is smiling and you say "Thank you very much for your time" and he says, "Anytime, come back soon, there was a nice stimulating rapport" . . . . AND ONE FINE MORNING . . . .

. . . . . And one fine morning you sit listening to the pumped voices in GREAT HALL and the words convey no meaning. And there is a knowledge that probably there was a time when you could hear such words and they could pass for meaningful dialogue, the way people probably do find meaning in the words of Humphrey, Johnson, Nixon. But once you see the lie the words fall vacuous, letters crumbling on the ground, like the letters of a foreign language, like the language of the moon . . . .

. . . . . . You sit in GREAT HALL listening to these words and it is like when you are talking with a friend by the lake and all of a sudden you are aware of the murmur of the lake, the chirp of birds, the bristle of leaves. The murmur and chirp and bristle have always been there, but it took a certain mood, a silence, to hear them and suddenly you see the words and they fall like blather and gibberish.

IX

You are in a one-bedroom apartment on 30th and Mission. In the apartment next door is Speed. Every night eight, ten, fourteen tough-looking guys and girls speed up and party. These are not the middle-class flower children frolicking in Golden Gate Park, these are lower-class white and they frighten you. They do not bother you but in the halls at night they appear, eyes tense, skin taut.

Down the hall Mike who attempted suicide last week lives with Alice and Marsha, and Alice also dates a Hell's Angel. The neighborhood is mostly Spanish and mostly quiet. You are with your girl friend Patty and you have no money. It is the summer of '68 and jobs are scarce in San Francisco.

You wake at 4:30 A.M. to line up at Manpower. You stand outside along the wall as the deserted street speckles with the shuffle of the drab and by six the envied garbage men with five-dollar-an-hour union jobs pass by eschewing the men of Manpower. The Manpower men spit or curse or silently glare and at seven the door opens and you march in and sit in the same order until you are called or until ten when the door closes and no more jobs are available. You sit waiting five hours for a job that never materializes and it is boring and horrid, but only a summer for you, for the men it is life. Manpower jobs and selling blood. They show their blood cards proudly, for if any member of their family needs blood, they'll get it. These are the drifters, the cripples, the dishonorably discharged. These are the nonskilled, nonunionized, nonbeings. They do not show up in census surveys and they are not randomly selected in Gallup polls, but they have traveled America and they know the price of blood. Mention Chicago and they shout, "Got paid sixteen dollars a pint there, not a bad city." Mention St. Louis, New York, Mobile, and they shout ten dollars a pint, twenty, eight.

And Patty is a GREEN BAY girl, grew up on Vince Lombardi and Krolls hamburgers. Huddled below zero cheering for the Pack and schooled in the Catholic Academy. The city derelicts depress her, the poor, the sordid, she has not yet inured. We can not afford the escape of a car, so we ride the bus and on a Friday night after seeing *2001, A Space Odyssey* it is depressing to have to ride the bus home. The faces haunt you, faces twitching, scabbed, lifeless. Bus people, they resemble New York subway people, sitting slapping their heads, biting fingers, talking to themselves, and you ride a half hour with men and women at midnight Friday when the San Francisco Broadway is just beginning and these men and women mostly Spanish and black have just finished cleaning buildings, washing dishes, and you have seen the lawyers and stockbrokers of Westchester and Stamford pull down the shades as they pass Harlem on the Penn Central Railroad and the bus has no shades and it is night and there is only the stink of darkness.

On Sundays you would ride the bus to Golden Gate Park and the fuming bumpy nausea of the bus would disappear in the magic of the green stretched in pleasure. You would play tennis or hike or mingle in the beat of ten thousand young gathered for a free rock concert and ten thousand flower children would dance and nod their heads and some were lovely free spirits radiating vital boundless beauty and others like the jaundiced boy nodding beside me were dying on heroin, dying on speed. And in an open field, children were playing baseball and a mom was strolling her baby and another mom was papoosing her baby and fourteen blacks were beating bongos as one white girl played flute. Patty and I lay in the grass as faces smiled, said hello, and offered marijuana and wine.

The Spanish hardware store man likes you and Patty and gives you twine and paint for free and brings Colonel Sanders Kentucky Fried Chicken and champagne to your house and he tells you of being a boy in Venezuela and traveling down the Amazon, almost dying from insect bites, buying women for cubes of salt, and suddenly you see yourself listening, you slow down to the speed of the Spanish man and you realize that you have been moving at the speed of MIFFLAND. You see words, your words, questioning the Spanish man on capitalist exploitation in Venezuela and you see the absurdity. Thousands of tribes, millions of people who never heard of Vietnam, never heard of the MOVEMENT. People whose language knows no word for guilt. People who only know subsistence. Millions of people living good honest lives and you are moving at the speed of MIFFLAND, moving at the speed of the MOVEMENT, and you must slow down, slow down and hear the Spanish man.

But it is difficult, you are boy becoming a man in a time of change and you are caught in the MOVEMENT. Caught in the rhetoric and hate. The MOVEMENT engulfs, spreads, and the intense search of becoming, of finding new space to grow in, becomes your life. You become blind. You lose touch with the people. You lose touch with the Spanish man.

You are in San Francisco slowing down, jogging Holly Park with Peanuts, the Spanish man's Great Dane, and you are picnicking in Sausalito and hiking the Muir woods and the MOVEMENT is far away, but the Spanish man gives you an old television and Patty is howling hysterically beside you and you are silent saturated with hate . . . it is Chicago the summer of '68 and the television projects the images triggering old dormant images and it is all coming back, you can feel your body speeding, intensifying and you have always hated when the radicals called the police pigs, always hated objectification, reducing people to slogans, things, gooks, niggers, hippies, pigs, but the images combust and the hate swells and there is Daley and you scream, "You fucking fucking pig, you fucking fucking fucking pig, you fucking fucking FUCKING FUCKING FUCKING FUCKING FUCKING FUCKING FUCKING PIG, YOU FUCKING

Melting

I

A nausea is sweeping the room and the room is
peeling yellow. You are spinning in a swoon and the
nausea is reaching out for you, pressing against your
calves and crawling up your thighs. The nausea has
engulfed your stomach and numbed your mind and it
was the same yesterday. And the day before. The
nausea is there, a smoke filming your mind, and you
can almost see it enveloping. You are trapped in
peeling yellow and there is no escape, except out, out
of the university, out of Madison, and the feeling is
not new, even last spring you phoned your mother to
tell her that you were wasting in the university, and
she began to weep softly at first attempting to con-
ceal her emotion from the office, but then loudly
unrestrained, for you see the week had been hard for
her, her days had been full of calls from her husband

quitting his job, calls from her mother crying because all her friends had died, calls from her daughter crying because she had miscarried, calls from the bank reminding her that she was eleven hundred dollars overdrawn, and it had all built up, this soap opera, just waiting for a call from her son telling her that he was dropping out of college, and she let go, she wept and hurt and I cried and hurt and she said that I couldn't do this to her, not now, and she said I had a history of not finishing things, and she said my father would be deeply hurt and I said what about me and she said what about her, what about him, and I said what about me, and she said I was selfish and reminded me of all the money spent and all the sacrifice, and I said I appreciated it but I didn't know it was a bribe, and she said it wasn't a bribe but I owed it to them to finish, and I said I couldn't live my life fulfilling other people's dreams, and she let go unburdening her hopes and dreams and disappointments and failures, she let go hysterically weeping my sister's problems, my grandmother's loneliness, she let go with her guilts and fears and sadness and it all weaved with the memory of my father dreaming, lying on his bed after work, his eyes exciting as he told of his new plans, his new business venture and how we'd all be rich, and for the moment he believed it, it was real, and I said what about me, and she said I only had one more year to go, it wasn't so much to ask, and she said my father would never understand, I was too much meshed in his dreams, and memory weaved swiftly, image after image sweeping my emotions, and I could see her there leaning over her desk weeping into the phone, tears I had seen so many times as a child, tears that had always made me cry, for I did not understand, but now I did, and I said what about me, but the words cracked hollow, I had been overwhelmed and I hung up to finish the semester.

In the fall I returned to Madison to try again, but peeling yellow captured me, it didn't take long, within a week I began to feel the waste of my days. Only now the waste grew and I began sleeping ten hours a night. I'd go to class a somnambulant and the nausea would envelop me, a stifling nausea, paralyzing my will, and I would go to the music lounge to study only to feel the oozing strain ride my legs and a need to rise and try the browsing library or the historical library or the cafeteria or the rathskeller, anywhere away from my mind. But there was nowhere to go, the rathskeller where I had gone so many times loving the flow of the become now appeared a tomb. My room was peeling yellow and the streets felt crowded, confining. Faces too familiar. Speech too predictable. Each day the same, an antsy roaming for peace. Playing the guitar, shooting pool, playing tennis could not negate the nausea, it was there I carried it with me, peeling yellow.

It had always been there, at least the knowledge that the university was wasting me, but this knowledge had been buried and balanced by the excitement of change, the radical culture forming. The Memorial

Union was my melting house, it was there that I had
sauntered through the halls as a freshman listening to
the debates around the political booths. My emotions
rising in anger as the boy shouting behind the End the
War in Vietnam Committee table ranted on about
American aggression. Slowly shyly I inched my way
up to the front of the forty people standing in a
huddle shouting, blocking the passage of the hall, and
as I said "Excuse me" I felt my throat tighten in acid
and most of the forty people were screaming at each
other, no one really listening to each other, just
immersion in emotions and the need for catharsis and
I shouted "What about China, what about China" and
two years later I would sit behind the booth with
pictures of Vietnamese children melting in napalm.

You loved the excitement of it all and when the
rock bands began spontaneous concerts on the Union
terrace it was vital and enthralling, it came out of
nowhere for free and you danced by the lake and
played Frisbee and this was your time, Union time, a
selfish time to indulge in becoming.

The Union was a fun house for us to distort ourselves in trick mirrors, and with the drugs trafficked
in the rathskeller we could ride every ride in Playland.
But you were too much of a perimeter to indulge in
drugs, too much of an earth child to fly, for even as a
child you preferred the ground to the roller coaster, it
was there on earth where the faces touched and
feelings melted, there where you got high on air, on
being alive. And just being there, being part of the
fun house distortion was exciting, just being there,

believing in the dawn. Just being there. But like the fun house in Playland where you sit on a large turntable which revolves slowly at first and then speeds up faster and faster spinning off the riders, eventually you reach a speed at which you must get off.

It no longer mattered if my mother wept or father wept, it no longer mattered if they did not understand, for now what about me rang solidly against the day and the night, what about me sleeping twelve hours a day, what about me peeling yellow, what about me unable to find a space to relax, a moment to shut off my mind and stop the waste. And if I was selfish or spoiled it did not matter, what about me mattered and if nothing else the MOVEMENT had taught me enough radicalism to focus on priorities and for now, for me, I needed out.

II

It is State Street, Madison, Wisconsin, in the time of
the trash. Goodman's jewelry store no longer displays
jewelry in the window. Rennebaum's drugstore no
longer has windows. The university bookstore, Dis-
count Records, and even the hip boutiques are
boarded up and aesthetically the glass was more
appealing, but you can write Power to the People on
the wood and draw pigs in multicolors. You are
sitting in front of one of the last plate glass windows
intact. You are sitting in Burgerville eating Burgerville
french fries and a Burgerville hamburger. You are
back in Madison after a year of working and traveling
and a mob of three hundred students wearing
bandannas is running toward you. The two girls and a
guy sitting at the table next to you back away and
the manager of the store closes the door saying "You

better go in the back, that window is going to go today, couldn't understand why they missed us last week, maybe they like our hamburgers." He laughs stalely and you smile, but you do not move.

Beneath the bandannas you begin to recognize a mouth, a nose, a chin, and you recognize a back, a walk, a run, and they are the movements of your friends, touch football friends and rathskeller friends, and there's Sandy from Yonkers who you dated when you were sixteen and in a movie theater she held your hands on her sweater above her breasts and it felt nice and there's Greg Donovan with a rock in his hand and his red hair waving in the breeze. His arm raises in the same easy rhythm of the powerful serve that made him a Michigan high school tennis star and his wrist snaps hurling the rock at you and the window cracks splattering to the ground as the rock flies past your face and slivers of glass fall by your feet and Greg Donovan is smiling, smiling abstractly and you hear him say "Put that in your pig burgers" and his smile pauses a second and then laughs loudly smiling at you. He draws closer extending a hand through the broken glass. "Hey man, good to see ya, what the hell you doing here" and he leans his head back laughing, his red hair sparkling in the sun reflecting in the cut glass. "This is really far out, huh" he says and you do not respond for you are not so sure how far out it is. There is a feeling in you that there is too much joy in the streets, and you want to question him, debate him, but you hear your words and they sound like ERIC SEVAREID, so you just stare pinning him in

71

your gaze against the sliced glass. "Hey, let's get together and play some tennis next week" he says and you say "Fine" and he says "Great, I'll give you a call" and he smiles slipping his head outside again and in the mornings on your bakery route you talk to the sixty-year-old salad and soup maker at Ella's Delicatessen and she does not understand why the students are trashing the stores and you try to explain it to her, you try to justify it for her, you try to rechannel her anger away from the students and toward the government, and at every stop you talk with the waitress, the janitor, the bartender and it is the same talk, the same justifying and rechanneling, but at home, on the streets, by the lake when you are alone or in the rathskeller talking to friends you are against the trashing and your feelings and loyalties are confused.

You are melting in emotions, melting between radicalism and life, ordinary life. Melting in the conflict between anger at the people on your route, their indifference, their fears, their prejudices and hates and love for them, their dignity and feelings and lives, and when you drove one spring morning past Kroger's supermarket and you saw it burning down you felt good. You had shopped there for years and it would be inconvenient to ride your bicycle over a mile to the nearest supermarket, and intellectually you were against the violence, but there was Kroger's melting to the ground and you felt good, you felt one with the people cheering.

You are sitting in Burgerville melting in confusion.

The Burgerville burger and the Burgerville fries are
not as tasty as the ones you ate in Al's and the faces
passing you, faces of the MOVEMENT, do not touch
you, they are moving somewhere, moving to violence,
moving to drugs, moving to food, moving to the
country, moving to Nirvana, moving somewhere, and
you are still here eating burgers and fries. Your friend
Helen tells you of her brother smoking marijuana and
tripping on mescaline and he is thirteen and you tell
her that you do not think it is healthy for him and
she says you don't understand the kids today, and
maybe you don't, maybe somewhere sometime the
MOVEMENT moved too far ahead of you, for you are
no longer moving at the same speed. The MOVEMENT
had been this great big space for a child becoming to
indulge in time and you did. And when you were
moving at the speed of this time, this time of melt
and flux, this time of radical awareness, this time of
journey, you loved it, you loved the excitement and
conceit, but now you were out of step and the
indulgence seemed like overindulgence. You spoke
with Jerry in the rathskeller about his parents and he
said "You gotta break all connections, they're out
there holding on, and they're not going to let go, I
mean you wont believe this but my father still thinks
I'm going to take over the pharmacy, no shit, and see
I'm into this trip, I'm really learning about myself
and I couldn't be here with them, they'd hold me
down, ya gotta break clean, it's the only way" and
you could understand, you could feel the need, for
you were part of the melt, but you were changing

along the perimeter, still bonded to the bourgeois world. You treaded tangent to the core, a perimeter flowing with the MOVEMENT, but always a perimeter, a line edging along the periphery of two worlds, two ways. You never joined SDS but you sat in the back of their meetings. You never joined the draft resistance movement but you told your father you would not serve in Vietnam and he said "If you're drafted you have to go" and you said "No" and so much of your radicalization was just that, not an extreme metamorphosis, but a melting of perception, a learning of another way. You were a young boy becoming a man in a time of change and the MOVEMENT came like a heroin through Harlem or a Christ it came a whispering of something higher, something finer, and its sirens sang in the depths of your impressions, but the MOVEMENT never really captured you, never swept you off the perimeter into its whirling center, perhaps because in your very core where the siren sang there were other songs, songs of your grandmother, old songs, sentimental songs, but songs, and they too could cast a spell and capture a young man in his becoming.

III

There was this time. A time of change and discovery. A time full of many becomings. Many soldiers died. Many students died. Many people suffered tragedies. Many people were unaffected by this time, their lives went on as if this time had never happened.

This could be any time, but it was not, it was America during the latter half of the sixth decade of the twentieth century. In five years a MOVEMENT had come and gone and changed a nation. The MOVEMENT had touched every breath of society, and if you happen to have been young during this time, an impressionable person, then you might know that even when the MOVEMENT dies or you move away from the MOVEMENT the MOVEMENT still lives . . . in you. Even if you are melting away from the MOVEMENT moving at a different speed, you know that life has changed and will never be the same. It is as if the LONE RANGER had come into your life and rode away. You might never see him again, might never even know who that masked man was, but he is there always an image in your life.

You are me sitting in the pulse of Agricultural Hall filled with students overflowing the seats, the aisles, and onstage is one man, a thin nervous professor who is not the most famous scholar at the university and not the most objective of historians, but when he opens his mouth you are overwhelmed. Overwhelmed by his flow of words, his eloquence, his knowledge, his language. Overwhelmed by his history. But mostly you are overwhelmed by him, his emotions, his feelings, his hates and his loves. When he speaks to you of the Vietnamese dead and the American atrocities, you feel the dead, you feel the anguish and horror of the living and when he tells you of revolutionaries in South America, in Greece, in France, revolutionaries who were tortured, killed, you feel his pain, and when he cries onstage, weeping through a story of sixteen Greeks shot for alleged treason, you cry too, and when he describes walking down a Calcutta street and the wretched starving people defecating, begging, dying, you are there in India, there in China, there in Latin America, you are there hating the dictators, hating the United States, loving the revolutionaries, loving him. The man could talk and feel and you are an impressionable boy radicalizing and he is someone to emulate and respect. And you are not alone, there are five hundred other people in the room and they

laugh with him and cry with him and rage with him
and ovation him. And in time they will outgrow him,
they will see him as too radical, too conservative, too
orthodox, too old, but that will not negate him, he
was there and he was important. He was a Jean
Brodie who could take a child at an impressionable
age and make it his if not forever then for a while. He
made you feel the wretched of the earth and the
feeling would subside in time and you would move
toward other feelings, but the feeling would never
fade away, it was always there to be triggered by the
words of a Nixon, by the faces of the government, a
vomit of hate and disgust, a vomit of contempt.

You are playing volleyball without a net and without a team and red and silver Frisbees streak by as
near you people lock arms dancing to the rock music.
It is a Mifflin Street street dance and there is no
admission and no boundaries. It is the MOVEMENT in
its purest form.

Some people are high on marijuana and some on
apple wine, but most are high on the day, the music,
the freedom. The faces smile past you and there are
moments when you touch and they feel good, but
mostly you are moving away from the MOVEMENT,
your eyes focus on an old lady sitting on her porch,
her hair is white and her face lined in Midwest wheat
and her skin hangs softly churned in Wisconsin
butter. She is old and a bitterness tightens her lip, a
butter molding beneath the gauze of screen and she
was sitting there before the MOVEMENT came with its
music and dress and drugs and violence and culture,

before the MOVEMENT came oblivious to her, never acknowledging her existence, her culture, and she leans, squinting, her lines etched in the blanched wheat of drought, dying wheat, before the MOVEMENT came reducing her to the same role America had reduced her, a rocking on her screened porch.

You focus on the dancing circle oblivious to her and you want to cry out, you want to shout hypocrites, liars; but it is too easy to turn on the MOVEMENT, to see its flaws and curse it. The MOVEMENT was everything, good and bad, and it cannot be dismissed. It brought a freedom and a hope. It brought another way. The faces you admired, the minds you respected, the people you loved, they were all MOVEMENT people, people caught in the change.

You are melting in the confusion of time and change, your loyalties and emotions are splintering, but if you found out that the LONE RANGER exploited Tonto, that he shouted "Hey chief, fetch me a beer" in Caucasian bars, you might turn against him, curse him for disillusioning you, but it would not negate his deeds.

Magic Theater
vs.
Middletown

I

We are talking then of a way. A road. A journey.
There has always been odyssey. Odysseus journeyed
and his son Telemachus must break away and journey
too. He must search and struggle. He may be
destroyed by the ocean or the enemies hoarding and
mocking his house, but he must dare, must journey,
must become.

We are talking then of a way. Drugs, Yoga,
Astrology, Science, Communism, Christianity,
Buddhism, Nudism, Magic, Meditation are all vias
leading, and there are many people who will find
themselves along one of these ways, but like the
MAGIC THEATER, it is not for everyone.

Harry Haller entered the MAGIC THEATER, but he
knew he was a lone wolf leading a trail. A trail that
would not be followed for many years, and when the

way was opened for traffic, when the MAGIC THEATER, condemned by bourgeois society, reopened, it captured a generation. Captured them as the expeditions of Lewis and Clark had captured generations before.

Go West Young Man, and you travel west riding the gentle rolling Iowa Nebraska farms. Rolling hills and flat lands leading to Colorado and Marlboro country. Riding curves up the Rockies and you are aware this is the West and the scope of the land thrills you. This is America and dreams were made in these panoramas, dreams born in the awe of mountains chained along the plains, and the desert mocking calling. There is a sense of danger and it is more than Gunsmoke, Paladin, Lone Ranger, it is there in the isolation, there in the vista beautiful but threatening, defying.

I stopped at a gas station in Oregon to ask directions. "Excuse me, I think I'm lost. I'm looking for the highway" I said. The affable gas station man said "You ain't lost, a half mile ahead, you were going the right way." "Right there huh" I said, and he smiled, slapped my thigh and chuckled nodding. And in northern New Mexico I stopped at an Indian craft shop. Spoke with the short-haired tough stocky white woman who owned the store. She told me of wealthy Indians and Mexicans discriminating against her. I was more sympathetic to the plight of the Indians and Mexicans than to the whites, but I listened, and when I was ready to leave she cut the price of two Indian drawings I was buying. And in San Francisco I worked construction and there was this big black man with big black arms and a huge black neck who drove a cement truck. We rode together in his truck and he asked me my name. "Andrew" I said. His big black face smiled a big black Negro smile and his laughter came from his big black Negro belly "My son's name is Andy too" he said. He asked if I were a student and I said "Yes" and the laughter deeper, richer, rose rolling from his mighty body and I laughed with him and he said "My son's a student too."

On The Road again, and not Kerouac's road or Kesey's road or Kuralt's road, but a road leading. There are ways. And there are choices. And there are new ways. And there are old ways. America was a way. America was a space waiting, a home for the primitive vision. And the adventures, the searchers, the rathskeller dwellers of old came to materialize their dreams. But somewhere sometime the dream got out of control and the clean beautiful space waiting became cluttered and uglified. Lies and greed mated again and again and spread westward engulfing a continent. The space misused, plundered, exploited, no longer held fertility for the dreams. The space captured by lie began to crack and in the cracks were streams and tributaries ... and ways. New ways for new explorers and in California at the end of the lie, the extreme space ruined by men moving at the speed of money, new ways began. Dotting the California highways were young explorers hitchhiking and traveling across the continent and searching along new routes with marijuana and mescaline and LSD.

Searching in Berkeley and Big Sur and San Francisco. New ways to love and live and relate and respond. New ways to make a life.

We are talking then of a way. Europe was a way. A very old way. And the young made their pilgrimages. In the fall of '68 you were wasting at the university. Feeling the motion of waste in your every action, every wake, every sleep, and the sleep insidiously crawled from eight to nine, and soon ten, eleven, and even twelve hours of sleep. And the need to get away, to get out, to travel and gain perspective and the need brought you to Luxembourg where you walked the cobblestone streets and narrow stone bridges, drifting in alone awareness, alone in the become. You met an orphan girl who invited you for a swim and you laughed with orphan boys playing soccer. It felt good to be free from MIFFLAND with its intense political awareness. Three years of becoming, journeying on a way and the need to stop the movement, slow down, saunter a different path. You hitchhiked to France, to Switzerland and you thumbed across the Alps freezing in the high snow air but loving every tactile moment.

You drank retsina dancing with men sailing to the Greek islands and you drank vino along the Italian coast near Napoli with a young couple who picked you up hitchhiking. The husband believed America was right in Vietnam and you tried to argue but he poured the wine and his wife laughed and you laughed and he laughed and after walking sixteen miles at night, with a thirty-pound knapsack on your

back, you found a small peasant village in Italy, and
the next morning walking down the winding hill an
old peasant woman in peasant dress and eighty-year-
old wrinkles in her round beautiful face, stood outside her door waving goodbye to you. She must have
seen you the night before and wondered who you
were, where you were going, where you came from.

And you walked the ruins of Pompeii touching the
walls, the murals, the jugs, and a Profound Feeling of
awe overwhelmed you. Here was Pompeii and the
walls still stood and you could feel the culture and
there was Vesuvius hovering waiting and how absurd
to be caught in the sterile flow of the MOVEMENT.
Caught in the conceit of the Messiah. Rationalizing
actions, nonactions, not rationalizing, just acting, and
here was Pompeii destroyed in a flash of nature, and
the same feeling in a graveyard in Milton, Wisconsin,
the tombstones engraved with names, Elder Hornsby
1823–1901, Gladys Holmes 1798–1869, and the profound awareness that under these stones were men
and women and children who had tilled the soil, cut
the timber, and they were mocking this twenty-
three-year-old dummy writing a book about America.
What did I know of these lives, these farmers in
Milton, what did I know of their way.

We are talking then of a way. Charles Kuralt is on
the road and he captures Americana in a nostalgic
romanticism. Peter Fonda and Dennis Hopper are on
the road and they see a different America, an
America of hate and money and sickness. The
MOVEMENT is on the road engaged in odyssey,

engaged in search, search for a way . . . .
. . . . And I am Goldstein boy becoming a man in a time of change. I have traveled the
way of New Rochelle and the way of MIFFLAND, and
I am somewhere there, somewhere on the fringe. I
travel the perimeter, for I am apart. I am bonded by
Al's and Fat Bertha. Bonded by old crippled men
walking three-legged boxer dogs. But I am alienated
from America, the government, the system, the lie,
and the liberal rational mind which sustains the lie. I
am bonded to the people and I live along the fringe. I
am unable to travel with the MOVEMENT for I am
not a true believer. I do not believe in the revolution.
I do not believe in Mao or Che. I do not believe in
LSD or Mescalito. I do not believe in cure-alls. There
are ways for some and ways for others. . . . The
MAGIC THEATER is not for everyone.

And there are times when I am jealous of the hippie
who plunges into drugs or the zealot bomber who
believes fervently in a cause. My mind is a critical
edge slicing belief before I can grasp it. It would be
nice to be the core, to plunge. To live the visceral
moments of belief. But I am of another breed. I
believe in friends. I believe in myself. I do not believe
in apotheosis. My emotions flow in I and Thou. My
sphere is the personal, the tactile.

And I and Thou are bourgeois emotions, and I am
bourgeois. I love the bourgeois emotions of family
and sentiment. I love hot dogs at ball games and bagel
pretzels in the park. I love movies and *Time* maga-
zine. I cry when basketball coaches retire. I cry at

every show of emotion, every hero. I love to flirt and charm and amuse nymphets. I have to throw darts at every fair and here's a quarter for two balls watch me knockem down, oh so close, here's another quarter, and I love my Mom and Dad.

I am in love with life. I have always been. I hop, I skip, I run, and the wonder of being alive overwhelms me. There is rhythm to my every stroke and it is not conceit, it is there in all of us at times, and the quest is to melt to timeless. I am I am cried the valley sheep man. I am and the wonder of being alive is an inarticulation. It is a feeling uttered not by language but by the physical embrace. I touch sand, the petal, the day, I touch you and we feel the beat. A gull glides, a stick feels good in my hand, a jellyfish wedges by my feet. Why is unimportant. It is. I am. We are.

I am I am I am and I walk the beach touching grains a million forms have touched before. Ten million years before there was beach and sea and sun. To be alive caught in the awe, in the immensity of life. And there is always a child drawing symbols in the sand and an old man searching for a special red shell. We are here along our ways and I am Goldstein one ego in a galaxy, one child becoming a man on the edge of a nation. On the edge of civilization.

We are talking then of a way. We are talking of the AMERICAN WAY and the AMERICAN ODYSSEY and somewhere along the way the road forked and the AMERICAN ODYSSEY and the AMERICAN WAY split. The roads diverged and curved and changed directions, but always the AMERICAN ODYSSEY is bonded to America, bonded by the past and the primitive vision. And you are an American radical on an odyssey away from America, but always it is an American Odyssey, America incessantly immutably defining your sphere. You can hate the government, rebel, curse, fight, but you are intrinsically American. You are Fat Bertha and five years of becoming in a time of change.

We are talking then of a way.

II

It is Madison the summer of seventy. David Sylvan
Fine is night editor of the *Daily Cardinal* and you
play tennis and swim in Lake Mendota complaining
of polluted waters. You laugh at Charlie Chaplin in
Modern Times and talk revolution on the terrace
eating Lay's potato chips and drinking Pepsi-Cola.
You live in MIFFLAND, the radical ghetto.

Beth lies naked on your living room floor per-
forming Yoga and telling you of her plans to live on a
commune in the fall. The summer before she was
smoking too many cigarettes, working as a nurse in
the university hospital and declining a proposition of
marriage from Tim, the doctor she was dating, for he
would only make fifty thousand dollars a year. She
was reading *Cosmopolitan* and *Vogue* and buying new
clothes every week. And somewhere sometime she

began smoking marijuana and protesting the war. Somewhere sometime she began to search and Beth is a GREEN BAY girl, grew up on . . . and somewhere sometime she began throwing rocks and was hit by a tear gas canister during the Kent State riots, and somewhere sometime she moved into a radical brigade and dropped out of school and dayed and nighted in the revolution. She is talking of women's liberation and the need to break down the roles and her body is graceful in Cobra bend, and now she stretches her spine and holds in the Plough.

It is Madison the summer of seventy and MIFFLAND swarms with hate. Susan says "Gotta get a gun." Chuck says "Gotta get a gun, man, the pigs are out to getya." Jerry says "Learning how to make bombs, heavy stuff." Beth says "Oo sometimes I get so afraid, you know, like the pigs know our house, you know, yeah um I just know one night they're gonna come and um, wow, is gonna be a bad scene." Beth is in Lotus now, her large breasts hanging and rising as she breathes slowly and her breathing creates a mood, a slow rhythm, a slow nakedness, and you can almost see the quiet permeate the room. I sit clothed in a brown chair and there is a feeling of melting M&Ms, I am here and there and here and there and MIFFLAND is arming itself for the revolution. . . . .
. . . . And there is this: There is Nino, his wife, mother, father, father-in-law, children, sisters, and everyday they work hard baking bread. Nino works from eight at night to eleven, twelve the next morning. On busy days the whole family sleeps

in the bakery. The baby Angelina plays on the bakery table as the family throws dough around her. The family laughs in Italian and screams in Italian and every day Josephine and Ancucia two little pixie girls are spanked for bothering the delivery boy. And there is this: There is you, Andrew Goldstein, waking at five every morning, working thirty hours a week while finishing your last semester of college. You are the delivery boy and you live in MIFFLAND the radical community two blocks away. And it is strange to wake in MIFFLAND, run two blocks and be in the old world. Strange in my last semester of college when friends are discussing communes, drugs, alternatives to marriage, family, to talk with Nino's pregnant sister who never heard of overpopulation, never heard of women's liberation. Strange to feel the flow of family so pervasive in the bakery.

Two blocks from MIFFLAND tribe of youth is a family working, laughing, and my college friends are freer, more intelligent, their way is more daring, more intense, but there is something there, something in the joy of making bread with your baby Angelina beside you to kiss, to tickle, to laugh when she smiles gumming your bread. Something there with your mother, father, wife, in a circle around the table, each working alone and together, rolling dough, mixing flour, putting holes in doughnuts and bagels.

You are Nino and this is your family. Your mother chases your father with a baking knife and you are Nino thirty-four years old and you laugh, this is your business and you work ninety hours a week and there is no time to relax, vacation, introspect, no time to question or plunge or journey, but your mother is pinching your arm as your daughters hide behind her apron and you are angry, but you laugh, and the children are saved from your wrath.

I stagger in before the sun at five-thirty and the two girls are sleeping clothed on a cot, and Nino's mother is sleeping on a couch and his father naps in a chair and Nino and his wife quietly slice dough rolling into loaves and there is something there, something we have lost in MIFFLAND . . . .
. . . . Beth stretches in the Bow, her hands grasping her ankles as she lies on her abdomen rocking softly in a cradle. She resembles a figurehead on the bow of a ghost ship appearing through a fog, and the quiet in the room weaves to the rhythm of her sway and she is a revolutionary. She believes in the violent overthrow of the government. . . . .
. . . . It is Madison the summer of '70 and somewhere sometime Mifflin Street became MIFFLAND . . . . somewhere sometime the love turned to hate . . . . somewhere sometime and I do not know when, perhaps when I was journeying in Europe, perhaps it was always there, but suddenly it was no longer just a radical movement, but a new society with divergent groups. People were going their own way and some worked at the co-op grocery, others at the Whole Earth Co-op. Others film clubs and Broom Street theater. There were communes and brigades. There was a tenant union and people were living on farms,

collectives, growing their own food, baking their own bread, smoking their own marijuana. Naked people touched in People's Park at night and on farms naked communal rituals. Thousands were experimenting with mescaline and the straights could no longer be told from the hip. It was incomprehensible to focus on five years before when there was no MOVEMENT, no drug culture, no youth violence, no youth society. The past was blurred an unreal time foreign to the new perspective and even four years or three years before, when the MOVEMENT was incipient, was an entirely different world .... somewhere sometime the MOVEMENT had ceased to be a movement, a cluster, and became the embryo in transition. Five years of change, fads, stages, non-violence, civil disobedience, violence, drugs, alienation, search and love and hate and contempt and repression and freedom and stage after stage a momentum building. Always even in the wanes a MOVEMENT capturing a generation, and gap and chasm and no return and always the search for new structures, new rituals, new ways, new space to fulfill the dreams and silences. New Pilgrims on the other side of America and there are no causes, no answers, there is only combustion .... somewhere sometime.

Faces pass me in a day wondering which way and I do not know, I only know I am witness and participant and tremendous change has occurred. A new society is incipiently forming and its language is foreign to the old. It is moving at a different speed.

I have heard the LIBERAL RATIONAL MIND OF ERIC SEVAREID and every night it articulates, every night it seems so right, every word so articulate, so eloquent, every word so rational. Walter says "That's the way it is" and every night it almost is, only it isn't. Every night the LIBERAL RATIONAL MIND OF ERIC SEVAREID misses the point. It articulates within the lie, within the liberal rational definitions. The mind is wound at forty-five, and if you happen to be going at thirty-three or seventy-eight, it is only the gurgle of a baritone frog or the tinseled inanity of Donald Duck.

Beth lies supine focusing on each part of her anatomy, breathing it to relaxation and she says soon she will no longer have time for Yoga. When school begins in the fall she will be totally involved with the revolution, organizing, writing and moving in the stealth of night in bands of two, three, seven, planting bombs. . . . . It is Madison the summer of seventy and David Sylvan Fine is night editor of the university newspaper and I do not know if our paths have ever crossed. But we were both in Madison the summer of seventy and perhaps we said excuse me as I walked out the door and he in. Perhaps we smiled and said hello sauntering by the lake. I do not know. I only know he was eighteen in the summer of seventy and when I was eighteen in the spring and fall of '65 I was broad-jumping twenty-one feet, running the two-twenty in twenty-three seconds, starring in the SENIOR VARSITY SHOW and writing a winning cheer for the

YELL LIKE HELL. I do not know if David Sylvan Fine is a bomber, but he was being hunted by the FBI for a bomb killing one, wounding two and destroying a math research building. I do not know if he is a good or bad person, I only know that he is not alone. He did not become in a vacuum. Nor did Leo F. Burt or the Armstrong brothers or Diana Oughton or Angela Davis or the Chicago Seven or the Milwaukee Fourteen or the New York Eighteen or every child dead on heroin.............................
It is Madison the summer of '70 and I feel alienated from my neighborhood. I feel the hate and outrage. I see beyond the lie and I know the lie must be stopped, but I am bonded by love and nostalgia and I cannot bomb. I cannot be a revolutionary. And as Beth talks of the fucking society I feel estranged, apart. Beth and others less bonded than I, more emotional, less personal, others who have emerged from the Jell-O are trashing and bombing and I cannot, but I have felt the need myself, here along the edge............................ And there are no causes, no answers, but surely in the combustion there was TIME. White middle-class appanage TIME but TIME to slow down from the speed of America. TIME to read and TIME to ponder. TIME to listen to music and TIME to trip on mescaline and LSD. TIME to smoke marijuana and talk feelings and dreams and TIME to free the body and mind and remove defenses. TIME to be open and vulnerable. TIME to search and touch. TIME to mingle in the flow of youth and TIME to become, to become a person.

TIME to dare and TIME to die. TIME to enter the irrational, the destructive, and TIME to be creative. TIME to enter the MAGIC THEATER and TIME to see the lie, slow down and view the neurotic frenzy............................ The children of the immigrants lived for the getting. The getting out of the Depression, the getting of money, the getting a home, security, and engaged in getting there was no TIME, no TIME to search and question, no TIME to dare. Life was defined by getting and there was no TIME to slow down from the speed of America, for getting was the speed, getting and getting and more getting until gotten and death.....

.... TIME granted by the children of the immigrants, appanage TIME and the children of the children of the immigrants and the children of the children of the children of the children of the immigrants and the children .... the children of TIME entered new TIME and new WAY........................

..... It is Madison the summer of seventy and people are moving at different speeds. Beth is slipping into her jeans and she says "Thanks for the dinner" and I say "Anytime" and she says "I've got to go to a meeting about um forming a defense group and um bumping off heroin pushers, you know what I mean" and she laughs nodding her pretty GREEN BAY face.

III

MIFFLAND is there like a memory, like a sometimes when, like a trying to remember. A life was defined. There was a routine. An order. The days were dry, dry days that could be put in canisters and sealed away. Sealed away for memory. Sealed away for . . . and now the days drip wet . . . . form- less. The days roll off my tongue in a wet whisper. In the whisper of sand rolling into ocean In the whisper of . . . and now the days drip wet and time has changed. And it is this, this trying to convey, this capturing of past, this driftwood, or rather more this bottle floating in the sea.

Drifting, west to Colorado, New Mexico, Oregon. Seventeen years of schooling and you are there, only time has changed and you are nowhere or only some- where, drifting . . . where to. A cottage by the sea, a coastal freedom to drift and think and alter the perspective. A time to measure time. An idyllic far away from the intensity of MIFFLAND, an idyllic place bordered by ocean and mountain, an idyllic time bordered by sand and forest. A frozen moment where time has stopped, at least MIFFLAND TIME. A space to saunter without fear and paranoia.

Drifting, searching, finding, and I speak to others young and old, drifting, searching, finding, attempting to put together something, some blend of East and West, some balance of yin and yang, some meld of old and new. There are hints and echoes of the latest ways—a hitchhiker passing through tells of Jesus—a letter comes with clippings of Berkeley and Madison—a friend of a friend builds a cabin twenty-seven miles from his nearest neighbor, deep in the Canadian wilderness—but mostly there is isolate time, time as always, beach time and ocean time and time to skip rocks and fly kites and throw yourself naked into the cold Oregon ocean and feel the flow—and only now and then, the memory. A black speaker in Madison shouting, "You ain't free, none of you, nobody's free until we're all free, I can never be free until my brother's free." A summer evening in Madison lying on the porch and the tear gas shooting, exploding on Mifflin Street and the police and National Guard troops charging down the street, a running again and again down windowless streets and the MOVEMENT sweeping. There on the wall of the post office are four FBI pictures of suspected Madison bombers and you leaf through the pictures, touching memory and it is all so distant, like a memory of a story, and how could this be, this five years of change, this time when you became a person, how could it be so far away.

My days, once so intense, now drift formless, slowly, molded by the moment. Days filled with sand castles and log walks and gull feeds. And nights along the wet cold with the stars close and bright, almost oppressively close, shining severely forcing you to confront their meaning, mocking you, engulfing you in their vastness. It is a time to redefine, a time to assimilate and understand and move somewhere.

The days drift further from MIFFLAND and even when the drifting slows and you are confronted with the reality that it is America 1970 and you are unemployed, MIFFLAND still moves further away. Jobs are scarce and this is not a San Francisco summer, this is a life and there is two hundred dollars in the bank and every day you fill out job applications and every week you stand an hour on the unemployment line and the faces of the men and women stare sadly, awkwardly, and they whisper of the next week, a good chance the mill will take on, and soon there will be a lot of logging, and there is the reality that you are no longer a bourgeois radical student, you are an unemployed man searching for a job.

In December you get a temporary job planting trees and you wake up at five to drive twenty miles to meet the crew at Dave's twenty-four-hour hamburger palace, and you drink a glass of chocolate milk as the foreman and eleven other men of the crew finish their breakfast. You all cram into a yellow van and ride for an hour into the woods. It is dark and foggy but as you ride higher day breaks through the woods and the panorama spreads along the broken fog. The men joke and laugh and as the truck swerves on the narrow slippery cliffs, they shout "Where the fuck you going Willy" and Willy laughs and the foreman tells of "This fuckin' nigger sitting in a booth kissing two white girls and nobody's saying nothing, kissing them in front of twenty loggers, well shit, no tree planter's gonna take that, I holler who the fuck does that nigger think he is, and this nigger stands up and Jesus Christ I'm shittin' in my pants, the fuckin' nigger is the biggest fucker I ever saw, bigger than what's that fuckin' logger's name over in Madras, Brockford, shit, this fuckin' nigger is bigger than Brockford and he's starin' right at me and every fuckin' logger is starin' right at me and not a one of them gonna budge when he busts the balls of this little old tree planter and I shout 'Go ahead kiss those girls, kiss my sister, kiss me' and the fuckin' bar roared" and the crew roars as the yellow van climbs.

It is raining and cold and you are climbing up and down hills with five hundred trees sagging on your hip. Up and down you go trying to keep up with the crew but the belt tears at your hip and you tumble falling forty feet cutting your hands and legs and every few minutes you slip on a log, a rock, the wet mud. Hours pass and your fingers bleed and your hip aches and you are aware that you are no longer aware of the beautiful scenery. Your body aches but you have worked harder jobs, construction in San Francisco, carrying bananas in Israel, but somewhere sometime something changed, for your mind could no longer accept this work.

You fall again the next day, losing two hundred trees, bruising your thigh and it is your mind, watching the faces, hearing the talk, your mind falling into a depression, your mind feeling oppressed, trapped, and these men, these high school dropouts and ex-convicts, these tree planters who talk of being men and fucking over other men and fucking women and fucking work and fucking life and fucking fighting and fucking fucking ball-busting rain, which is now pouring, these men who drink every night and move in packs of six eight twelve on the weekends into bars to drink and crash with loggers who hate tree planters, these men who drink their nights and travel through Oregon and Washington away from family and friends, travel with the crew eating in hamburger palaces and sleeping in cheap motels, these men know who they are, they know they are the drudge of America, they know and feel the oppression. These men who live in alcohol and fantasy are the crew and I am the crew and this is my reality and it is overwhelming in its oppression and they want out and I want out and no matter how much you search for meaning and dignity in their lives, always there is the oppression pervading and you are the one member of the crew who can get out, out of the van, out of the shit, out of the oppression. Out.

It is your mind and it wants out. Afterward it will

become a humorous anecdote about the time you lost two hundred trees, but now it is an oppression, a reality that you are the one member of the crew who has choices, the one member who is still becoming, still defining, and even you are trapped. Trapped by money, trapped by definitions, trapped by time, and you want out, out of being the seasonal laborer, out of the unemployment line, out of the compromise, and you are out of the bourgeois world, out of money, and you are out of college, out of MIFFLAND. You are out of New Rochelle and out of the Bronx. You are drifting somewhere, somewhere in a limbo between outs and you know that someday you will have to be in.

DRIFTING, somewhere, and it seems that most of becoming has been this limbo, this waiting for in. Schooling for, dropping out, traveling, searching, becoming, and in the summer of '70 you are done, the limbo has ended, only it has not, you are still drifting, out.

Out of work, out of money, and it is a time to redefine. Out of MIFFLAND, out of five years of becoming and where to. You have become during a time of change and there is no place to go, except THE DRIFT. The youthful siren calling, THE DRIFT, the nether limbo that waits for you. You can settle in Oregon or California, you can travel back to your roots in the East or you can go to MIFFLAND, but it will all be part of THE DRIFT. THE DRIFT is your home for now, for there is nowhere else to go. You have become during a time of change and you are that change and the only space available for that change is in THE DRIFT. THE DRIFT welcomes you and shouts "Come on in" but you know that THE DRIFT is out, a finite temporary place for those who dare and THE DRIFT can be fun and exciting, THE DRIFT can teach you many things, but if you drift too long you become a prisoner of that space, an astronaut forever circling the moon.

IV

IV

Fat Bertha is watching. Watching me. Watching you. A deaf child named Amy is winking on a beach in Oregon and five years of change, five years of becoming. I am Goldstein boy becoming and Fat Bertha is watching.

I am a perimeter walking a beach in Oregon at the edge of America; but even in the thick curdling cheese of Wisconsin I was here along the edge. Five years of change and I have changed, but I am not one who plunges. I am bonded by love and nostalgia. Bonded by family, which flows through my blood.

I walk the beach of Oregon and silver sandpipers ice-skate the shore and two old ladies walk slowly scanning for agates. Before me is beauty, the ocean transforming every second into lovely design, and giant trees sculptured and twisted by the ocean lie majestically conquering the beach, their roots bending in tension and power, capturing the space, defiant, permanent and immobile until a greater power, the ocean storming, will sweep them up like toothpicks.

I pick up hitchhikers down Highway 101, young products of the MOVEMENT and I feel so alienated from them. From their inarticulation, from their nonverbal ways, their minds. We ride down the coast, admiring the beauty, the shade of sand, the splashing wave, but basically we have nothing to say. They tell me of their marijuana bust, their Jesus, their commune, but we are not of the same sphere. I read the *Wisconsin Daily Cardinal* and the tales and editorials on revolution bore me. And these searchers espousing Jesus and these children smoking marijuana, what do they know of me and I of them? And who will be the God tomorrow? Who will be the new Messiah to lead us in our lost? And who will be the God tomorrow?

Sometimes I yearn to be that superstar, to rekindle GOLDSTEINISM with new tenets and new believers, to hand out keys to MAGIC THEATERS and launch naked ships to naked seas. But then I remember the flow of the become, I focus on the Miffland softball game where every Friday afternoon in the summer ease the hip radical boys who burned Kroger's supermarket in the spring and smashed First National's windows in the fall would choose sides and Fred, the third baseman who made it a point to let you know he smoked grass in-between batters, shouted "We want Kellerman" when Kellerman strode by with his big

mustache and confident walk, the walk of Kellerman
the ex-fraternity home-run king, and when the
radicals on the other team shouted "You just took
Vanders" Fred the third baseman shouted "You can
have Vanders, we want Kellerman" . . . and it is bad I
think not to believe, or to believe that there is no
hope, no cure-all. In five years of becoming I have
seen too much despair. With all the Gods and highs
the despair was always there, not just ovulating,
waiting, but there sucking energy. A malaise paralyzing and pushing searchers into new journeys, new
becomes and new Gods. . . . And who will be the God
tomorrow, or does it really matter, I do not know, I
am one person in a galaxy, one person obsessed in
becoming and from my eyes so much is exterior,
ephemeral, but there are things you know as you
know the day, as you know your name, and you
know that even if tomorrow the Gods changed and
the people forgot Vietnam and drugs and Rock and
youth and culture, even tomorrow if the earth blew
up and we began again on the moon, and even if
Nixon and Humphrey and McDonald's came, these
five years of becoming could not be negated. Yes,
even if the new Messiah were ERIC SEVAREID, even
then there would be echoes of what was, and not just
the crass and superficial, not just the exterior lies, but
the vision and intent, the hope, even then, even there.

Five years of change and I have changed. I no
longer move at the speed of MIFFLAND. I see the old
man wearing red sneakers playing bridge. I speak to
the Oregon real estate agent with an American flag

pasted on his window and I espouse the smile of that old lady in Italy who smiled wondering who I was, where I came from, where I was going. I am here now where I have always been, playing hopscotch in the sand with a deaf child named Amy. She smiles pixie eyes, twirls and falls laughing to the shore. I fall too. She screams pointing ahead, rising in the sun running to the blue jelly in the wet sand. She points and I mouth   Jelllll   lleeeeeeeeee   fishshshsh Jeellllllllleeeeeeeeee   fishshshsshsh   and she repeats my words and touches the blue and loves the feel. She giggles and touches again rebounding with the spring of the jell and we run laughing along the shore far from five years of becoming. But I am aware that my very running, my very mind and body movements are all wound in five years of becoming threads and Fat Bertha threads and Grandma threads and American threads and Vietnam threads and MOVEMENT threads. My very time is a MOVEMENT time, granted by the new ways. My approaches to the sand, my relation to the ocean, to the faces, to the day, are a meld of Fat Bertha and five years of change.

Five years of change and I have changed. I am part of the MOVEMENT I could never go back to the old perspective. I have known and been part of the feeling of hate and rebellion and there are many in five years of change who plunged and are now revolutionaries or communalists or dead. Many who have totally removed themselves from the main culture attempting to build structures of a new society. I am still a perimeter for I cannot negate my family and I find meaning even in bourgeois lives. But as much as I am still bonded, I have not gone full circle, my perimeter is not a circumference. I am a part of that generation that was granted time to experiment with time and somewhere sometime we changed the time clocks of ourselves. We altered our beats and entered new time and new way .... And who will be the God tomorrow, I do not know, but I look forward .... Forward to becoming.

Meeting

We meet again, you and I, far from Al's candy store in the Bronx, far from the IF men who in their wildest IFS could never have dreamed that the little boy eating hamburgers and fries would be a farmer in California. Far from Miffland and far from that time of change. A farmer harvesting oranges and olives, a farmer rising before the summer sun to disc the fields and ridge the soil in preparation for an irrigation where the farmer will shovel dirt eighteen hours building dams to force the water across the trees and in the star breeze of 2 A.M. the farmer will rest beneath a eucalyptus tree and feel his arms and legs aching and the feeling will be nice and he will sit in an irrigation ditch cooling off the sweat and the feeling will be nice.

Farmer Goldstein will climb eighteen-foot leaning

ladders to pick oranges and he will stretch his hand
for a sumptuous fruit hanging in the green and a
supporting limb will break tumbling Farmer Goldstein backward twenty feet down where he will land
on his head and the feeling will be nice. Not so nice,
but nice, for it is a time of melding and Farmer
Goldstein loves lying beneath the shade of olive trees
and he loves the faces of his wife and friends smeared
in dirt and he loves the feel of his walk as he
barefoots through the mud or strolls in the evenings
with his wife and dogs and the moon filters through
the orchard rows and all is silent except for the cows
staring.

Time is slow, very slow and there are no days, not
really, not even Sunday. There is only daylight and
darkness, there are lists and chores but the days meld
into each other.

There are no sidewalks, no stoops, no suburbs, no
mingle of the melt. There is only land and the land is
your time. Your space is not filled with the touch and
smell of strange bodies and I am a city boy so I miss
the flow of life. But there is land to breathe into and
mountains to explore. My wife and I pick oranges in
the hot sun, both dressed in our Big Mac overalls and
a neighbor comes by to buy fifty pounds of oranges
and he hollers to my wife mustached in sweated dirt
"Hey sis, don't let that big bully work you too hard"
and he laughs and she smiles and he tells us how
delicious our oranges are and it is all very pleasant
and on the road when I am pruning trees or resting in
the high grass the driver of every passing car waves

hello and it is all very superficial, this friendliness, but very nice. There is something in the recognition, in the positive confrontation, something in the waking up to stroll down the orchards unencumbered by negative confrontations, to walk with my wife to the mailbox, to walk with a friend to fix a gopher hole, something in the gentleness of the walk, the day.

We meet on a wind machine high above the orchard, you and I. The two twelve-foot propellers are spinning as we revolve slowly scanning the farms and mountains to the east and west and in the north we see Mount Shasta covered in snow, a hundred miles away. There is a feeling of power up here, the engines roaring and the height dwarfing the trees below. A feeling that we could fly like SUPERMAN if we wanted to. We could be that cure-all battling backward-talking men, but we are in THE DRIFT searching for a perfect meld and aware that SUPERMAN never found it. With all his powers he could not meld a harmony. He roamed Metropolis a schizoid drifting back and forth between Clark Kent and SUPERMAN in a never-ending battle against himself. His consciousness was that of a speeding bullet and he never questioned why a person might not want to move faster than a speeding bullet. He fought for truth, justice and the American Way, but he never found himself and even if he had lived on a farm it would not have changed him. Even if he baked organic bread and lived in a commune with Lois Lane and Jimmy Olsen he still would have hid in closets changing costumes.

There is another feeling up here, a feeling of melding with the sky and the mountains, and you and I. A feeling of breathing in the day and touching you, and I am more of this feeling. There is a movement to the country, a searching for the good earth, the basic needs, the stripping to essentials, but farmer Goldstein is not part of it, his flesh was not molded in soil. He was born of concrete and his roots are not trees but subways and sewers. Farmer Goldstein is a point on a graph, neither plus nor minus, just a point on the line of becoming. An articulation of some sort of consciousness, some meld of Fat Bertha and the MOVEMENT, but the farm is not the meld, only the milieu. The farm is a space for an approach, a perspective.

I am of this other feeling, this wanting to touch you and the day, to touch the very contact of our lives, and so I walk orchard paths and feel the thrust of my person meshing with the earth and the feeling is good and Patty and I go to a neighboring barn dance and it is a lovely constellation night and there is joy in the approach as we walk touching, breathing in the smell of night and grass and cow and mulch and rural evening. The barn lit in the night distance and the country western music floating over the fields, this could be anytime in the history of America, and we are one with the limbo of the moment, the smell and feel of a barn dance approach. It is a mostly middle-age and elderly crowd of farmers and it is strange to be here. An old toothless farmer in his late eighties is dancing with the few young girls, stamping his feet in a rocking motion as he spins across the floor, and people laugh with the toothless grin, proud of his nimble body. He dances with Patty, who is shy and embarrassed. She dances stiffly at first, self-conscious. But the old man is oblivious to her timidity, lost in his abandon, and she too is soon swept into the toothless charm. Around the floor laughing spinning and other dairy farmers and sheep ranchers and almond growers laugh too and I am aware that a few years before we would have been enemies and it is overwhelming to confront this knowledge and to comprehend that my life has moved again and I am here, this child of the Bronx and New Rochelle and MIFFLAND here dancing at a barn dance in Rural America and in Oregon we played rummy with Levi and his wife, both in their eighties. Levi, who worked in the same sawmill for forty-five years and could still slice kindling wood with one elegant stroke of his aged wrist. He told me of being a boy on a farm near Eugene and his father would give him a dime on July Fourth, a nickel for the hayride into town and a nickel for fireworks. I try to comprehend the totality of Levi and this toothless farmer, the immensity of their lives, and for the moment it does not matter whether they are bigots or reactionaries, for in whatever systems these lives dwelled, there was always the possibility for contact, for a rummy game, for a western dance, always the option of touching. So I am torn, for I am more of this feeling, this wanting you.

And it is true that Farmer Goldstein enjoys his

image, enjoys the overalls, work shirts, heavy boots. He loves the sound of Farmer Goldstein and enjoys envisioning himself as a free spirit becoming, an American Gypsy experiencing the land. He loves mingling with other farmers talking olive prices and orange problems. Loves driving the 1942 Chevy truck double-clutching as he delivers thousand-pound bins of fruit and loves weaving the orchard on the big red International diesel tractor.

And it is true that he wants to think of the farm as a statement of his freedom, a manifestation of his radical consciousness. He likes to rationalize his life into the vanguard of the MOVEMENT. Enjoys telling people that he sells organic oranges to the Berkeley conspiracy and that he joined a committee to organize the olive growers. But when his father calls and says "Hey farmer, when are you coming home" that is real and the myths and illusions are shattered. When Patty worries because they can't afford a dentist and they argue over taking the dog to the veterinarian, then the manifestation of radical consciousness seems very minor.

When the big radical intellectual farmer sneaks into the house after pruning trees, to catch up on "Love of Life," Patty laughing affectionately says "Hey Vanguardo, come lie with me" and he laughs and she laughs pleased with her cleverness and they lie embracing, talking of Kate's baby by Rick even though she's married to Dan, and Matt Corby in jail for murdering his wife and Van may go back to Bruce because she could never marry Matt now, even

though he was once her husband before he suffered
amnesia and I find that when friends visit to tell me
of their Yoga or organic diet, to tell me of their way,
the only way, the cure-all of our time, I cannot
tolerate their voices. Yet I believe in Yoga and
organic food as I believe in the MAGIC THEATER, but
not for everyone. There is something in these lives,
these bourgeois lives that wave hello and sell me three
dollars' worth of lumber, something worthwhile and
valid as any guru. So I go fishing with my neighbor's
children and we trade oranges for squash and a girl
named Tanya aged five listens to me play C major and
A minor chords on the piano and she closes her eyes
in an almost swoon and says "Play that song for me
again, it made me feel like walking through the forest
and sitting by a tree listening to the wind" and we
meet again you and I touching somewhere in our
becomings.

And there are smells, sometimes just near the barn
where an olive wind whirls the eucalyptus leaves and
rusted barbed wire leans sadly on peeling fruitwood
and I am compelled to sit and smell a notion, a
feeling. My body floats higher in love with the
wonder of the moment and the notion is of a
memory streaming fondly, vaguely, a memory of
another time perhaps my own perhaps yours and then
I walk slowly, flanked by black and white Holsteins
waiting to be milked and black overripe olives waiting
to be oiled and I am aware of myself and the day and
it is this union with life that is my God. A feeling
sometimes in the split of wood, in the aroma of an

ozone evening, in the touching of you. A feeling of joy in the wonder of becoming, in the moments of contact and relation.

Patty and I cheer the high school wrestling team and I play basketball on Wednesday nights and she volleyball on Mondays and yes we are bourgeois as hell, but that is where we meet now, in this meld of radical bourgeois consciousness, and I really don't know if it is all bullshit, but I like to think it isn't.